GOD,

THE ALTERNATIVE CURE
A Journey of Faith and Hope

D1253415

May God richly bless you or your journey.

Lerry Hornstein

GOD,

THE ALTERNATIVE CURE
A Journey of Faith and Hope

Terry Hohenstein

NEXT CENTURY
PUBLISHING

Published by Next Century Publishing
www.NextCenturyPublishing.com

ISBN: 978-162-9038377

Printed in the United States of America

Dedication

Long before I was married, God placed a desire in my heart to be the best wife and mother I could possibly be. Ever since He gave me each of those opportunities, that desire has grown immensely.

As a Christian, I have another desire that is constantly growing in my heart, and that is to leave a legacy with my children and their children of knowing and trusting God and desiring His perfect will for their lives, above all else. Although I have a long way to go in all of these areas, my sole purpose in writing this book is to encourage my family to follow God's leading—to listen for His voice.

His will for each of our lives is something He planned before He formed us in the womb, and it is the very best plan for us. I want each of my family members to be willing to step out in faith when God leads them to do so, knowing He's their safety net—nothing can touch them unless He lovingly allows it.

Because I know I have missed opportunities to share the amazing things God has done and continues to do in my life, I want to put some of these stories in writing, so they will be there for my children and their children to read, especially if God places something in their lives that they think they can't handle. "All things are possible with God." He is our strength and our courage. He will increase our faith and enable us to accomplish His goals for our lives.

Toward the beginning of my ordeal with cancer, a dear friend gave me a little pillow that has the following inscription embroidered on it: "The Will of God will not lead you where the Grace of God cannot keep you." Oh, how I love that! Just let the truth of that sink in, and then believe it with all your heart.

I dedicate this book to my precious husband, Kenny, who has been with me through better and worse, in sickness and in health, in the most selfless and loving ways imaginable. He has been such an encourager and tower of strength and always knows how to help me regain my focus.

I also dedicate this book to my amazing daughters, Selena Garrison and Kristen Hohenstein. They have both blessed me in so many ways and have made me proud beyond my greatest expectations. Thank you, both, for your love and encouragement and for always striving to be the best that you can be.

Additionally, I want to dedicate this book to my mom, Mildred Cox, and my sister, Sandra Milner, who played such an integral role in my recovery. I'm so thankful for your determination to personally participate in my "walk through the valley of the shadow of death" through fasting and praying for me and with me on a daily basis. Thank you, both, very much.

Last, but certainly not least, I want to dedicate this book to my wonderful son-in-law, Curtis Garrison, and the most amazing grandson on the planet, Emmett Garrison. Thank you, Curtis, for loving your mother-in-law and always blessing me with your sweet compliments about my cooking. Thank you even more for being a loving husband to Selena and a wonderful father to Emmett. I know God is going to greatly use you in the ministry to which He is leading you and Selena.

Emmett, darling, when you are old enough to read this, I hope and pray that Jesus is already residing fully in your heart and life and that you desire to be all that He has planned for you to be. In addition, I pray that you will always seek to be more like Jesus every day.

I treasure each of you more than you know.

All my love,

Terry, Mom, Nina

Table of Contents

CHAPTER ONE

Background

For years, my husband, Kenny, has been asking me to write a book about my breast cancer experience. For all those years I've said, "Why? Who would read it? Nobody wants to do what I did."

To which he would reply, "It's not just about what you did, but about all the things you experienced along the way. Those experiences could really encourage someone else going through a similar difficulty."

I would brush the idea aside, knowing that I didn't even have time to *read* a book, much less write one. I figured that the Lord would provide the time and the desire, if He ever wanted me to pursue that.

Recently, after trying to find me for many years, Dottie Coffman, an old friend, located me on Facebook. Our families attended the same church in Coral Springs, Florida, during my breast cancer diagnosis and subsequent treatment. Two years later, Dottie had her own breast cancer ordeal, but I was unaware of it because she and her family moved away not long after my experience, and we lost touch. After moving to Atlanta, Dottie had become a radio talk show host, and she wanted to interview me about my unconventional cancer treatment.

We scheduled the interview, and while Dottie and I were talking just prior to the interview, she asked whether I had thought about writing a book. When I told her that I had not, she said, "You really need to write a book, Terry. It could be a real encouragement I said, "Funny you should say that, Dottie. Kenny has been telling me the same thing for years."

I mentioned Dottie's comments to Kenny, who would normally say, "Why is it when I suggest something, you always say 'no,' but when someone else suggests it, you think it is a good idea?" (Unfortunately, it does seem like I do that to him—sometimes.)

To my surprise, he said, "Terry, I totally agree with her. You really should consider writing that book. Just try to carve out a little time here and there. You never take the time to sit down. I think it will be very therapeutic and relaxing. You are not under the gun to get it done by any specific time, so just work on it whenever you feel like it."

Having never written a book before, I had no idea where to start; but I guess, like any storyteller, I need to start at the beginning:

***

I was born in January, 1960, in Miami, Florida. I was raised in a Christian home and asked Jesus into my heart as a young child. Being part of a godly, Bible-believing church has always been a wonderful and important part of my life. Having a church family that loves and supports its members and is willing to be there for them in sad times and happy times is an amazing blessing. My husband, our two daughters, Selena and Kristen, and I were members of that kind of church—Cornerstone Baptist Church in Coral Springs, Florida.

As I look back over my life at all of the wonderful churches we attended, Cornerstone really stands out in my mind as a *church family* that focused on discipleship and fellowship, with a pastor that focused on equipping us to live our lives victoriously in Christ. My Cornerstone family played an integral part in my cancer battle and victorious outcome. My most precious friendships were forged at Cornerstone, and my greatest leap of faith, so far, was taken there.

I turned 35 in January, 1995, and knew that "35" was the magic age for a baseline mammogram. I dreaded that mammogram but scheduled it nonetheless. The mammogram was not as bad as I had imagined, and several days later I received word from the doctor's office that everything was clear. I breathed a sigh of relief.

A few months later, I noticed one morning while shaving my legs that my right leg was numb. *That's weird,* I thought, but just figured a couple of trips to the chiropractor would take care of it.

After six weeks of treatment and no change in the numbness I was experiencing, my chiropractor sent me to a neurologist, who ran some tests and, in turn, sent me to a rheumatologist for some in-depth blood work. When all the results were in, the neurologist called me back in and told me he suspected I may have multiple sclerosis, lupus, or some other type of autoimmune disease. At that time my only symptom was the numbness in my right leg, and he didn't want to subject me to a lumbar puncture (spinal tap) for that single symptom.

He told me that it might just be some nerve damage that needed time to heal. It just so happened that our Rottweiler/Shepherd mix had accidentally knocked my feet out from under me in our backyard about two weeks before I started feeling the numbness, so the doctor's thoughts on the possibility of nerve damage made sense and were a great comfort to me. I was told to return should new symptoms arise.

Roughly a year later, on a Wednesday morning in June 1996, I was on my way to work when I was rear-ended at a red light. It didn't seem like an awful jolt; neither I, nor the other driver, seemed hurt, so we took each other's information, and I went on to work. As the day wore on, I realized I had whiplash. My neck was hurting pretty badly by the time I made my way home.

I could have easily excused myself from going to the Wednesday night church service, but our pastor had been preaching a wonderful series from the Old Testament book of Ecclesiastes titled "Poise." That night was the final segment, and I did not want to miss it.

Many people are familiar with the most popular verses in Ecclesiastes 3:1–8. The lyrics from a very popular 1962 song titled "Turn! Turn! Turn!" were taken from this passage. The song was written by Peter Seeger in the late 1950s. Although the Ecclesiastes passage is well known to most Christians, the popularity of Seeger's song allowed these verses to become familiar among the unchurched as well:

1) "There is a time for everything, and a season for every activity under the heavens:

2) a time to be born and a time to die,
   a time to plant and a time to uproot,

3) a time to kill and a time to heal,
   a time to tear down and a time to build,

4) a time to weep and a time to laugh,
   a time to mourn and a time to dance,

5) a time to scatter stones and a time to gather them,
   a time to embrace and a time to refrain from embracing,

6) a time to search and a time to give up,
   a time to keep and a time to throw away,

7) a time to tear and a time to mend,
   a time to be silent and a time to speak,

8) a time to love and a time to hate,
   a time for war and a time for peace." (NIV)

The main focus of my pastor's sermon series on the book of Ecclesiastes was to equip us as we entered into each new season of our lives, whether good or bad, to be able to weather that season with *poise*. Webster's definition of *poise* is: "[1] to hold (something) in a balanced and steady position, [2] to be drawn up into readiness."

So, the purpose of the series, was to teach us that whether the storms are raging around us or the sun is shining down on us, we need to live in such a way that others can see us gracefully holding "steady" in our faith and "ready" to respond in a positive manner to whatever God brings our way.

Toward the beginning of the series, I asked the Lord to please give me poise and help me display it in my life. I had always been impressed with godly women who consistently seemed to say the right thing and respond in the right way, who never got rattled—women who took life as it came, with faith and grace and dignity. That's the kind of woman I wanted to be. Little did I know how much this sermon series and my prayer were going to come into play in my life in the next few days, weeks, and months.

When we arrived at church that evening, we greeted our friends and settled into a pew. We sang a few songs, had prayer, took up the offering, and then Pastor Bill began to preach. I struggled to pay attention, because my neck began throbbing with pain that seemed to be radiating into my chest and both of my breasts.

Later that night I was lying in bed, and with great trepidation, I checked around for lumps. My left breast seemed fine, but the entire right side of my right breast was as hard as a rock. I turned to my husband and said softly, "Kenny, have you ever felt this before?" He told me that he had not and said, reassuringly, that maybe it was caused by the accident.

The next morning I called my ob-gyn's office, and he said to come right in. While doing the breast exam, he explained that breast tissue is very sensitive and even a moderate impact could cause a fibroid. That is what he was hoping this was, but just to be safe, he sent me to the hospital for a mammogram because their machines were the most advanced.

So off I went, thinking all would be well in a matter of an hour or two. I didn't even call my husband to update him. I decided I would just tell him when it was all over; I could give him the good news that he was right—it was just a fibroid caused by the accident.

When I got to the hospital, I was ushered promptly in for the mammogram. The technician was a very nice woman who didn't waste any time; she had a calming effect on me. When she was finished, she told me to wait and that she was going to develop the films and make sure she didn't need to take any more pictures before I left.

She was gone for a very long time, and when she finally returned, it was with a look of concern. She told me to go ahead and get dressed and that the radiologist wanted to see me right away. The calming effect she had had on me earlier was quickly replaced by panic.

As I dressed quickly, my happy-go-lucky mood drained out of me. When I saw the radiologist, she showed me the films, which meant absolutely nothing to me, of course. She pointed to a large white mass in my right breast and said, "Do you see that?" I quietly said, "Yes." She said, "That is not good. This is very serious. You need to run—not walk—to a general surgeon ASAP."

I said, "Do I have cancer?" To which she replied, "As I said, this is very serious; you need to get to a surgeon immediately—today, if possible."

It was already late in the afternoon. I'm not sure how my shaking legs carried me back to the car. I didn't have a cell phone. I couldn't call my husband or my ob-gyn. I sat there in my car and sobbed for a long time before starting for home. I needed to contact my doctor before his office closed at five p.m. to find out which surgeon he would suggest. I could barely see through my tears to drive.

What was going to happen to me, to my husband, to my children? What if I had a mastectomy and my husband left me because he thought I was ugly? I had heard that story before. What if I died and my children were left without a mother? I had not heard of anyone on either side of my family ever having breast cancer. How could I have it? Why would I have it? I had always taken fairly good care of myself. I didn't smoke. I didn't drink alcohol. I was a few pounds overweight, but nothing serious. So many thoughts were rushing through my mind.

When I finally arrived home, I quickly called the doctor. He said he would contact the surgeon for me and try to set up an appointment for the next day. I called my husband at work, and he came home immediately. I will never forget the first thing he said when he burst in the door. I was sitting on the couch crying with my head in my hands, and he came over and gently took both of my hands and looked me straight in the eyes and said, "Terry, no matter what, I will be here. I will always love you, and you will always be beautiful to me—*no matter what!*" Well, the Lord knew what I needed to hear to get me through the next several months, and that was it.

We then needed to tell our children. Selena was ten years old; Kristen was six. They were next door at our neighbor's house. Katie picked the girls up from school for me in the afternoons and kept them until I got home from work each day. We didn't know how to tell Selena and Kristen, except to relate concisely what we knew, which wasn't much, before they heard bits and pieces from someone else. We also sought to assure them that everything was going to be okay—even though we weren't sure whether that was true.

It was very difficult, but we plunged in with the news. They both looked stunned. Kristen was the first to speak, "Are you going to lose your hair, Mommy? You can't lose your hair!" She started crying really hard, and I told her I would get a pretty wig, and she and Selena could help me pick it out. That didn't comfort her. She cried even more hysterically. I held her and told her that some people don't lose their hair, and maybe I would be one of those people. We would pray for that. After a while, she was finally able to calm down. Selena just took it all in quietly. I worried about what was happening in her pretty little head and heart.

CHAPTER TWO

Cancer History

I met with the surgeon the next day, Friday afternoon. He was a gentlemanly, older doctor with very kind eyes. My ob-gyn had sent the films of my baseline mammogram with me. When the surgeon compared the two mammograms, he showed me that the mass was clear on my original mammogram. He could not understand how I could have been given a clear report a year earlier. Me either! My left breast showed no signs of any kind of density, but the X-ray of my right breast showed this incredibly large mass that just lit up the film—the same mass the radiologist had pointed out to me the day before. Ominously, the mass was now much more pronounced.

The doctor performed a needle biopsy, explaining everything as he went. It was virtually painless—just a pinch that lasted a few seconds. The needle was hollow. He inserted it into my breast and through the mass. When he pulled the needle out, the tissue needed for the biopsy was encased inside. The results would be in on the following Monday. In the meantime, because of the size of the mass, he told me it was going to have to come out, whether it was malignant or benign. He called the hospital and was able to get the surgery scheduled for the following Thursday.

I called from the surgeon's office to let my husband know so that he could take time from work to come with me to my doctor's appointment on Monday. When he got home from work that night, he informed me that both of his bosses had told him he could not miss work on Monday if he planned to take off on Thursday for my surgery. Kenny was devastated and so angry that he wanted to quit. I told him not to worry, that I was sure my mom could go with me, and that would be fine. I just didn't want to go by myself. That didn't make him feel any better, but what could we do? We didn't know what the future held, and jobs weren't easy to come by. He couldn't jeopardize his employment.

The next morning, Saturday, I woke up with a jolt, remembering that I was scheduled to sing a solo in the church service the next morning. I had purchased a beautiful accompaniment track for the song, *How Great Thou Art,* several weeks earlier when I found out I was scheduled to sing. I had been practicing with the track diligently until the accident, but everything started happening so fast after that, I had completely forgotten about it. Now, I started wondering how I was going to sing such a powerful song with so much emotion going on in my life. I cry so easily—a sappy commercial can set me off; how could I get through a song that overwhelms me with emotion, even when nothing serious was going on in my life?

I knew I needed to talk to God about it. "Please, Lord, give me the strength to deliver this song in such a way that your message is clearly heard. Please help me to hold my emotions in check, and let nothing hinder whatever You plan to accomplish through me as I sing. Thank You, Lord, in advance for enabling me to do this. In Jesus' name, Amen."

Girded with renewed strength, I put in the accompaniment track and began to practice. As soon as I got to the chorus the first time, I broke down sobbing, so I kept practicing over and over, until I could sing it without crying. I kept quoting, "I can do all things through Christ who strengthens me."

The next morning when I got up to sing, I felt a sweet peace flood over me. I began singing and felt my spirit being lifted up with every word. It was a beautiful experience until I noticed a dear friend, who had arrived late, rushing in toward the back of the church. She looked up at me, our eyes met momentarily, and then she put her head down and began to weep. THAT WAS IT! All of a sudden I felt like Peter, when he was walking on the water and took his eyes off Jesus, and suddenly began to sink. I was sinking.

My whole being welled up with emotion, and I could not get another word out. The tears started flowing, but the accompaniment track kept on going without me. I did not want the message of the song to be lost, so in an effort to salvage what was left of the song, I quickly asked the congregation to join me in singing the rest of the song, which they did, gladly!

When the song was finished, rather than returning to my seat, I went straight back to the ladies room and had the heart-wrenching cry I had been holding in for several days. Then I quietly returned to my seat for what was left of the pastor's sermon. At the end of the invitation, my pastor asked me to come forward. He told the church of my appointment the next morning to get my biopsy results and my upcoming surgery on Thursday. Everyone held hands and prayed for my healing.

That afternoon, I began pondering the whirlwind of the past few days. I started thinking about my family history and the people who I knew that had died of cancer.

* * *

A Family Haunted by Cancer

From the time I was a young child, I worried that my dad would die of cancer. He smoked cigarettes, and I knew that smoking caused cancer and cancer killed people. My dad was also a heavy beer drinker.

Interestingly, I recently read an article on www.washingtonpost.com that stated, "Although doctors have long known that women who drank more than one drink a day were more likely to be diagnosed with breast cancer, the new analysis (recent findings in a large Harvard study) marks the first clear evidence that even those who consume that amount or less are at increased risk."

I'm sure if drinking can cause increased risk in women for breast cancer, it can also increase a man's chances of having different forms of cancer, besides the obvious cirrhosis of the liver.

I always thought my dad was an alcoholic because he drank heavily on his days off. Someone I know who *is* an alcoholic told me he didn't think my dad was an alcoholic but, rather, an habitual drinker. Apparently, there is a big difference. I do know that when my dad decided to quit drinking, he just quit. He didn't seem to have any withdrawal symptoms whatsoever. I don't know how young my dad was when he started smoking and drinking, but he did it until he was well into his sixties and then, one day out of the blue, he quit both.

My dad was fair-skinned and bald. He worked nights for Eastern Airlines and would spend the early part of the day outside, cutting the grass and working in the yard. He always had a nice tan, despite his fair skin. In the summers, we would go to the Florida Keys and swim, fish, and water-ski all day long. There was no sunscreen in those days; all of us would get sunburned.

Dad started having problems with skin cancer before I was a teenager. He began wearing a baseball cap and long-sleeved shirts when he worked in the yard, but the damage was done.

When I was 15 years old, he underwent an extensive surgical procedure on the top of his head. This included a skin graft that left a really ugly scar. It was sad, because my father was a very handsome man, and that scar really marred his good looks. Since I was as fair as he and I never wanted to have skin cancer, I started staying out of the sun. When all my friends wanted to go to the beach to lie out and tan, I started saying, "No, thanks." The few sunburns I have had since then have been purely accidental.

My dad's father was also a smoker. I remember receiving a letter from him during the close of my first year of college. He told me he had lung cancer. He had been undergoing chemotherapy and radiation for a while, but it wasn't going well. He hoped to live until I could see him. He said nobody else wanted to tell me. They were afraid it would interfere with my college studies, but he didn't think that was fair to me. He felt that I had a right to know. I was so glad he told me, but I was devastated.

By the time I was able to get home to see him, he was in a coma at the veterans' hospital in Miami. On our way to visit my granddad, my father tried to prepare me. I had never seen anyone in the last stages of cancer. Despite my dad's efforts, I was completely unprepared for what I experienced.

The smell of the VA hospital was sickening. I was truly shocked that those who were willing to sacrifice their very lives for our freedoms by serving in our military had to receive their treatment in such a place; they deserved the best of care. The state of the place disgusted and hurt me.

When I entered the hospital room, I saw that my grandfather, who had been a tall, strong man only months earlier, had withered down to about 80 pounds. I could see the outline of his frail body under the thin sheet. He appeared to have shrunk to 5 feet in height. I would never have recognized him. His face, like his body, was skeletal with skin tightly pulled over it. Oh, how my heart ached! How could this have happened to my grandfather in the short time since I saw him at Christmas? He passed away, just hours later, at the age of 80. That was the summer of 1979.

Many years later, my father and I were once again making a dreaded hospital visit. My father-in-law (Kenny's foster dad, Bob Wickersham) was dying of multiple myeloma, a cancer of the blood that spreads through the bone marrow. He had been diagnosed three years earlier after cracking his ribs trying to climb onto the back of a jet ski. When chemotherapy and radiation were recommended, I remember thinking, *Oh, no! Once he starts that, he'll never feel good again. That stuff just kills people!*

Unfortunately, my prediction proved true; but this time, I witnessed it all firsthand.

At this time, Kenny, the girls, and I were living in a cute little two-bedroom, two-bath townhouse that we purchased when we were first married. Selena was born on our third wedding anniversary, and Kristen was born four years later. While I was pregnant with Kristen, we put the property up for sale, but it didn't sell. Right after Kristen was born, a couple from our church asked if they could buy our home. They needed to close before their wedding, which was coming up in a few weeks.

We agreed to sell but didn't know where we were going to live. My mother-in-law, Caroline, suggested that we move in with them and take our time finding a new home. She was working full-time while also taking care of Bob and her aging father, Granddad. She thought it would be a blessing to all of us to help each other out, and she was right.

I was able to be home during the day with my little ones but also keep an eye on Bob and granddad. I took care of their needs during the day while Caroline and Kenny both worked. I tried to have dinner ready when they arrived home, so Caroline could relax a little before launching into everything she needed to do for Bob.

I watched my father-in-law deteriorate. He was sick every day, but some days he was able to get out a little. The chemo made him terribly ill and weak for

28

several days after each treatment. As soon as he started feeling a little better, he would have to go back for another treatment. I felt so bad for him and for Caroline. She was a wonderful caregiver, but I knew her heart was breaking.

Nine months after we moved out of their house, Bob went into the hospital for the last time. My dad called me one morning saying he would like to go visit Bob that evening, so we went together. It was difficult, of course, and was a grim reminder to both of us of my grandfather's death.

As we were leaving the hospital, my dad said, "Terry, if I'm ever diagnosed with cancer, you, your mom, and your sisters need to know I will not have chemotherapy. I do not want to die like Bob and my father."

I thought for a minute and then said, "Well, if you don't have chemotherapy, what will you do?"

He said emphatically, "I will live until I die."

The next afternoon Caroline called to let us know that she didn't think Bob would make it through the night. Jason, their son, was on his way home from Gainesville, and she hoped that he would make it before Bob passed away. We made plans to get to the hospital as soon as Kenny got home from work. When we arrived, Caroline met us at the door to Bob's room. She told us he was in a coma and wasn't expected to live much longer.

We visited for a little while and were so relieved when Jason arrived safely. We felt that it would be best for Jason and Caroline to have some time alone with Bob, so we sadly said our good-byes and left. A few minutes after Jason was able to let his dad know that he was there and that he loved him very much, Bob slipped into eternity. That was May 7, 1991.

CHAPTER THREE
Diagnosis and Surgery

Five years later, on a Monday morning in June 1996, my mom and I made our way to the surgeon's office to find out the results of my core biopsy. While waiting in the doctor's office, Mom shared with me that she had been fervently praying for me, and she felt positive that my tumor was benign. I, on the other hand, had also been fervently praying, but I strongly felt that the tumor was malignant. Nevertheless, God had given me peace that it was going to be okay.

When the doctor said, "Mrs. Hohenstein, you have ductal carcinoma," and started to explain what that meant, I was at peace; but I could see the color drain from my mom's face as she sat next to me. She didn't say anything, but I could feel her devastation. I heard the surgeon say that ductal carcinoma was a better diagnosis than glandular carcinoma; he elaborated further, but that was all I heard. Finally, the surgery that had been scheduled for four days later was confirmed.

When I arrived at the hospital early Thursday morning, June 13, 1996, my mom, my sister Sandy, my pastor, and many of our church friends joined Kenny and me in the waiting room to pray before my surgery. After our prayer time, a nurse came with a wheelchair to escort me to the surgery suite. Sandy asked if she could accompany me, knowing how difficult it is to find a vein in my arm for any kind of blood work or anesthesia (she has the same problem). She was hoping to keep me distracted during the IV process. Thank God she came with me, because it ended up being the worst phlebotomy ordeal of my life!

When we explained to the anesthesiologist (a very pleasant young man, probably early 30s) the kind of problems that technicians usually have finding my veins, he said not to worry; he didn't expect to have any problems. Well, after strapping my arm, slapping the top of my hand, and endlessly poking and prodding with the needle until tears were streaming down my face, he took a deep breath and said that he was probably going to have to surgically implant the needle in my hand. But he was going to have to take a break first and come back in a few minutes. I thought, *Wait a minute...*who *needs a break?*

Ironically, the anesthesiologist never returned. I guess he was so stressed out, he had to go home—*I wish I had that choice.* Another anesthesiologist took his place and was able to get the needle in without a problem. Whew! That was a blessing.

Prior to the surgery, my surgeon explained that he intended to perform a partial mastectomy (he was very conservative and did not want to remove the entire breast) and a lymph dissection. This meant he was going to cut me from the mastectomy area to my armpit (the lymph glands) and remove all of the lymph nodes that looked "sick."

After surgery, he explained that when he got to the lymph nodes, there were four in the front that looked malignant. He removed those, as well as three directly behind them that had a normal appearance. The removal of the additional nodes was to ensure the ones remaining were healthy. A drain was implanted in the surgical site near my armpit, and the doctor said it would come out the following Monday. I spent the night in the hospital and was released the following morning.

The drain was the most difficult part of my recovery. It seemed that every nerve ending in my entire body was attached to that drain. If I moved at all, it caused a searing, burning sensation in my armpit and breast. Because I had both of my babies with absolutely no medication, I consider myself to have a very high tolerance for pain. The pain from that drain, however, was excruciating. I don't know if that is normal, or if it was going right through a nerve or in an especially sensitive area, but I could not wait to get that thing out.

My precious husband was the most amazing caregiver. During my recovery, when he was not at work, he never left my side. His concern was so evident, and he was incredibly gentle with me in every way. He could not do enough for me.

I believe with all my heart that a loving, devoted spouse often endures more emotional pain than the one who is actually going through the physical trauma, when a couple is dealing with something like this. I also need to say that, even though we were surrounded by so many loving, caring, and giving people, there was never a time during this whole ordeal that anyone thought to ask Kenny how he was doing or offer to comfort him. He was not only trying to help me with my emotional and physical pain, but he was also dealing with the fears of our children as well. He quietly placed his needs on the back burner.

I mention this not to sound condemning, but rather for the sake of awareness. We could not have been surrounded by more wonderful people. Because of what Kenny experienced, he has become more sensitive to the needs of a spouse or caregiver in circumstances such as these. He makes sure to ask how they are doing and if there is anything he can do to encourage or help them.

At the time of my diagnosis and surgery, I was working at an accounting firm. I have to say that God has always blessed me with wonderful work environments. One thing I truly loved about our office was that we had this big kitchen with a nice long table where most of us would congregate for lunch every day. It was great to be able to sit and talk about our families, sports, and current events and really get to know each other. We were friends, not just coworkers. Consequently, my work "family" became very concerned about my cancer diagnosis, surgery, and recovery.

All four of the accounting firm's partners had beautiful boats, and every year, after tax season and toward the beginning of the summer, the firm would plan a long weekend at a lovely resort either in the Florida Keys or on Florida's west coast for the partners, employees, and their families. We would enjoy boating, fishing, water skiing, swimming, and all of the fun stuff that the combination of a resort, boats, and the ocean could offer.

It just so happened that the long celebratory weekend for this particular tax season, which had been planned months in advance, fell on the week after my surgery. Everything happened so fast with my diagnosis and surgery that I didn't even realize until my surgery was over that my family was going to miss out on the weekend that we had been looking forward to for so long.

Of course, there was nothing that could be done about the circumstances, but as I was pondering my family's loss of a wonderful time, my dear friend and coworker, Eileen Bitzer, called. She said, "Terry, I was wondering how you and Kenny would feel if my family took Selena and Kristen with us this weekend. I would hate for them to miss out on all the fun, especially when I know how much they have been looking forward to it. We would take really good care of them, and it would be a great diversion for them. I'm sure they could use some fun times about now."

I broke down and cried, of course, because that's what I do. Kenny was close by and said, "What's the matter, babe? Who are you talking to?" I told him it was Eileen and that her family wanted to take Selena and Kristen with them for the weekend. He said, "Wow, that is amazing! Tell her 'YES!' and 'thank you so much.' I hated to tell them we weren't going to be able to go, and now I don't have to. They are going to be so excited!"

They were thrilled when we told them and couldn't stop talking about all the fun they were going to have. Kenny and I were both so happy; they had something exciting to look forward to. Eileen's family picked them up very early Thursday morning, just a few days after our telephone conversation, and they were on their way to Sanibel Island. Kenny and I shared a sigh of relief, knowing they had a few days to just be kids and enjoy kid stuff, rather than feeling the weight of the serious issues we were facing. Although we made a strong effort to stay lighthearted and positive in our conversations, they could sense our concern. Never discount the intuition of your children. They know.

While the girls were gone, it came time for Kenny to change the dressing on my surgery area. He had already been helping me bathe and take care of the drain, ever so carefully and gently. I felt so helpless and even embarrassed that he had to do these things for me, but he seemed truly thankful for the opportunity to help me.

I will never forget how anxious I was when he removed the dressing from the mastectomy area for the first time. I did not want to see what I looked like, and I certainly did not want him to see what I looked like. The thought of it had been haunting me since well before the surgery. When we pulled the bandages off, I gasped in disbelief at my deformity.

From my perspective, I looked hideous. I had to look away and wondered how my husband would be able to still love a wife who was so deformed.

He said, "Terry, that doesn't look bad. I'm just so glad you are alive. That is all that matters to me."

What an awesome blessing God had given me in him! Kenny's positive reaction and reassurance of his love for me overcame my first big hurdle—his acceptance of the new me.

Eileen and the gang all arrived home late Sunday afternoon with golden-brown tans and big, happy smiles. Both of my beautiful blonde girls were even more blonde after spending so much time on the beach. It looked as if they had streaks of sunshine in their hair. Eileen and her daughters had been so careful to keep them lathered with sunscreen, and we were so thankful for their diligence in keeping our girls from getting sunburned.

Eileen, her daughters, and Selena and Kristen presented me with a beautiful lamp with a glass base that they had filled with the gorgeous shells they picked up on Sanibel Island. Everyone on the trip joined in to find some pretty shells to fill the base. The girls were beaming as they told us of all the fun they had searching the beach and the sand bar for those pretty shells and little starfish for Mommy's lamp. I still treasure that lamp and the sweet memories my dear friend and her family made possible for my children that weekend. Friends are a blessing from God.

CHAPTER FOUR

Leap of Faith

The next crucial event came the following morning, with my follow-up appointment to remove the drain and hear the postsurgical pathology report. Kenny had once again requested time off from work to go with me, but his boss informed him that he already missed work for my surgery, and he could not miss work again. Once again, he was livid, but I told him not to worry. He was able to be with me for the surgery, and my mom could go with me for this. As it turned out, my mom and Sandy both went with me on Monday.

When we arrived at the doctor's office, we had to wait a little while—of course. I was so anxious to get that drain out that even the short wait seemed unbearable. Finally, the doctor called us back to a room and removed the drain. What a relief! I honestly felt like a new person once that horrid intruder was removed from my body. Once I was freed of the drain, I was to get dressed and meet the doctor in his office to hear his recommended postsurgical treatment plan.

Once we were in his office, he explained that the pathology report revealed a very aggressive form of cancer that had spread to my lymph glands. In his opinion the cancer was between stage III and stage IV (stage IV being the worst), but he felt certain that he had removed all of the tumor and the malignant lymph nodes. The extra nodes that he had taken were clear, but because of the aggressive nature of this type of cancer, he had already spoken with an oncologist and set up an appointment for me to meet with him.

The oncologist was suggesting a new, very powerful chemotherapy called "stem cell replacement chemotherapy." My surgeon was happy to say it was the newest and strongest chemo on the market, and I was a perfect candidate for it. While he was imparting this *awesome* news, my insides started churning; I wanted to vomit. He then told me he wanted to help me understand what chemotherapy does and how this new therapy was different.

He explained that a cancer patient has both healthy cells and unhealthy cells. The purpose of chemotherapy is to kill the unhealthy cells. Unfortunately, it kills many of the healthy cells as well; that is why people get so sick and lose their hair, etc. Because this new chemo was so powerful, it would destroy virtually all involved cells. The "good news" from his perspective was that prior to instituting the chemo regimen, a certain amount of my "stem cells" would be removed and preserved.

After the chemo killed both healthy and unhealthy cells, the stem cells would be reintroduced. Hopefully (key word), my immune system would be strong enough to allow those preserved stem cells to reproduce and *voila!*—IF I were lucky, I might be cured. All I could think was, *WHY WOULD ANYBODY DO THIS TO THEMSELVES?*

Well, somewhere during that excruciating explanation, I felt the Holy Spirit say to me (not in an audible voice, but in my spirit), "Don't worry about any of this, Terry. This is not the plan God has for you."

When the doctor finished his recitation, he gave me the oncologist's name, told me to call to confirm the appointment, and said he would be seeing me for follow-up. As we were getting into the car to return home, Sandy said, "Terry, we are going to be by your side through all of this. It's going to be okay."

When I turned to her and my mom and said, "I'm not doing any of this," they both looked at me in a complete state of shock.

They asked in unison, "What do you mean, you aren't doing any of this?"

I explained to them that I wasn't sure *what* I meant, but that the Holy Spirit told me God had another path for me. I didn't know what that would be, but I *did* know it was not what we had just heard from the doctor. We drove home in silence. After lots of long hugs, my mom and sister returned to their own homes, and I called and canceled the appointment my doctor had made with the oncologist.

The next morning my mom called and told me she had a book she wanted me to read. A friend from our home church in Miami had called her, after she returned from my doctor's appointment, and said she felt the Lord impressing her to give me this book. My mom had stayed up all night reading it, and now she wanted to bring it to me. I asked her the name of the book and what it was about; she told me the title was *A Cancer Battle Plan* by Anne Frahm, and it was about a young woman with breast cancer who followed a nutritional plan for her healing.

I said, "I don't know, Mom. That sounds a little extreme, not to mention frightening."

She quickly replied, "Well, you said you weren't going to do what the doctor laid out for you, so maybe this is the path God wants you to take. All I'm asking is that you read the book and keep an open mind."

I said, "Okay, Mom. I can do that."

Because I was still recovering from surgery and had not yet returned to work, I was able to start reading the book as soon as my mom brought it to me. I was immediately taken by the fact that both Anne Frahm and I were 36 years old when diagnosed and had two children, ages 6 and 10. I felt an immediate kinship with Anne.

As I continued to read, I felt a sense of peace permeate my rattled soul. I kept sensing the Holy Spirit gently whispering, "This is the path God has chosen for you."

Anne's first symptom was pain in her shoulder. Her doctors misdiagnosed her several times, allowing her cancer to spread uncontrolled. By the time she was correctly diagnosed with breast cancer, it was very progressed and had metastasized to several other areas of her body. Chemotherapy and radiation were started immediately and went on for two years. Nothing seemed to slow the progression of the cancer. As a last ditch effort, she was admitted to the hospital for two weeks of intense treatment.

By the end of those two weeks, she felt her body was burnt from the inside out. Layers of her lips had peeled off, and her mouth was full of blisters. The cancer had continued to spread in spite of everything the doctors had tried. They sent her home knowing she had only a very short time left—possibly days—to spend with her family.

When she arrived home, completely spent, a friend was waiting there. She said she knew Anne was tired, and probably didn't feel up to this, but she had someone she really wanted Anne to meet—someone she felt could help her. She had made an appointment for Anne and was hoping she would be willing to go. Anne asked her friend who it was, and her friend told her it was a nutritionist. As tired as she was, she knew she had nothing to lose, so off they went.

The nutritionist laid out a plan of action, and Anne was willing to try it. At the end of 30 days, Anne's doctor ran additional tests, and she was *cancer free*. I was ecstatic. I knew that my situation was not as dire as hers, and if God could work that miracle in her life, He could certainly do the same for me. Because He was leading me down this path, I had to believe that it was His will to heal me completely.

As hot tears streamed down my face, I prayed, "God, you know how badly I want to live. I'm not afraid to die because I know I will be in heaven with you for eternity, but I want to be here for my husband and be able to see my children grow up. I'm willing to do whatever You want me to do, regardless of how hard it may be. I know that You will give me the strength to do it. Please help me, God. I know this is the path You want me to take, but I don't know any nutritionists. Will You please lead me in the direction I need to go to find the right one? In Jesus' name, Amen."

Well, within minutes the phone rang. I wasn't surprised because my phone had been ringing off the hook day and night since my diagnosis. When I answered, I heard a woman's voice on the other end of the line.

"Hi, Terry. I know you don't know me. I'm new to your church. My name is Dana Morgan."

The funny thing is I had noticed Dana at church a couple of weeks earlier and had asked some mutual friends who she was. I learned that she was from a church they had previously attended. They told me she was a single mom and that she was a real sweet girl, but she was a little wacky. When I asked what they meant by wacky, they said, "She only eats nuts and twigs." I had no idea what they were talking about. Who can survive on nuts and twigs?

They had laughed at my obvious confusion and explained that she didn't really eat nuts and twigs. Dana was deeply into nutrition and healthy living, and they liked to tease her about it. I didn't think much of it at the time, but, of course, I was very intrigued by her phone call.

As we talked, Dana told me that she heard I had been diagnosed with breast cancer and was possibly looking for an alternative treatment. Wow, news travels fast! She explained that she felt God impressing her to call and tell me that she had a wonderful nutritionist and would like for me to schedule an appointment with him. She knew I would like him and felt sure that he could help me.

I'm not exaggerating when I say that I almost dropped the phone. I was speechless. God had answered my prayer *instantaneously*. He was making it so clear to me that His hand was all over this because He knew how much I was going to need every one of these little miracles to look back on for confirmation in the days ahead.

I nearly yelled as I exclaimed, "Are you kidding me?"

She was startled, and asked, "Have I offended you?"

"No, no, no. You are not going to believe this, but I was just asking God to lead me to a nutritionist, and as soon as I finished praying, you called. This is just incredible."

When Kenny arrived home from work that evening, I met him at the door. I could not wait to tell him all about the book, and what I felt God was leading me to do, and how He had already opened the door for a nutritionist. I excitedly poured out all the happenings of the day, and Kenny was amazed. He said I should see the nutritionist as soon as possible and that he would join me in the treatment. He felt that was the best way to encourage me and keep me on track. What a keeper!

I called my mom and Sandy. They were both thrilled with what God was doing and said they would join me, also.

CHAPTER FIVE

Opposition

I think I can safely say that no "leap of faith" comes without some opposition. My friends at church were mortified at my decision. Many were in the medical field, and they thought I had lost my mind. They adored my husband and children and were afraid that this was a death sentence. I knew they loved me intensely and wanted the best for me, but all they knew was medicine. They didn't understand.

I started getting phone calls each day, all day long, from well-meaning friends begging me to do what the doctor advised. One dear friend met me in the church parking lot on a Sunday afternoon as I was walking out to my car. I guess she felt compelled to talk some sense into me, since no one else had had any success with that. She pleaded that I stop thinking about myself and start thinking about my husband and children. She knew I was afraid of chemo and radiation but stated that I should overcome it, or I was going to leave my family without a wife and a mother.

I was stunned, of course. Not only by *what* she said, but also by the fact that she said it in the first place. It was all I could do to keep from saying, "Of course, I *care* about my husband and my children. What are you thinking?" Instead, I calmly explained, "Listen, I know that you are scared and that this doesn't make any sense to you. I know that you are saying this because you love me, but God has made clear to me the path He wants me to take, and I'm going to take it. I don't have a choice. I'm not going against Him no matter how many people disagree with me."

The next morning I received a call from my dear, sweet pastor, Bill Overstreet. He said he had been hearing about some decisions I was making and wanted to get the information firsthand. I told him in detail of the Lord's leading in my life, and once I had explained everything, he said, "Terry, I commend you for following God's leading in your life. I know this is a huge step of faith for you and that it is not going to be easy. You certainly don't need the stress of your church family coming against you, even though they mean well. You don't have to worry about anyone from church discouraging you anymore."

I have no idea what Pastor Bill did, but from that day on my church family was for me and did everything in their power to support me. I will share some of the incredible things they did for me a little later.

Within a day or two of the call from Dana, I was able to get in to see the nutritionist. Once again, my precious mom went with me. I knew from Anne's book that I needed a special kind of nutritionist. Before I wasted any of his time, I wanted to make sure that I was on the right track. I told him that I had read *A Cancer Battle Plan,* asked him if he knew of Anne Frahm, and asked if he practiced that type of nutrition.

He said, "Yes, I know Anne, and that is exactly the type of nutrition I specialize in."

I then asked him, point blank, "How many women with breast cancer have you treated that have survived?"

He smiled. "I've treated lots of women with breast cancer, and all of them have survived, to my knowledge."

Well, that was great news. "Where do we start?"

Jesse—the nutritionist—laid out a plan for me that was nearly identical to the one in Anne's book. He told me we would start with a 7-day organic vegetable juice fast. I would drink only water purified by reverse osmosis and organic vegetable juice. That would be followed by a very strict 30-day plan. On the 30-day plan, I would be able to eat organic fruits, vegetables, and whole grains. In other words, I became a vegan, which is the strictest form of vegetarianism.

There would be no dairy, no sugar, no meat of any kind, and no processed food in my diet—but there would be a lot of supplements. After that 30-day period, there would be some blood work that would need to be done to confirm that I was cancer-free. I would then continue the vegan lifestyle for the rest of my life, although the amount of supplements would decrease somewhat after the 30-day plan and then continue to decrease as my immune system became stronger.

His belief in this plan gave me confidence as well. My only concern was how we were going to be able to afford all of this. I needed so many small appliances that I didn't have (a juicer, a steamer, and a bread machine among other things). In addition, I didn't know where we would get the money to buy all organic foods and supplements. We were already on a very tight budget. However, little did I know, God was already working on answering those questions and providing for those needs.

My friend, who had confronted me in the parking lot just a few days earlier, got together with many of the ladies at church and organized a "Shower of Love" for me. God had turned the tide. My church friends wanted to supply me with everything I needed to get started with this nutritional plan.

The shower was an open house, and the ladies came bearing gifts. I opened the packages, and we prayed together. The entire afternoon was filled with prayer, encouragement, and blessings on my family. Kenny, Selena, and Kristen were at the shower also, and they were given gifts as well. It was such a beautiful outpouring of love and support from my church family. I received all of the things that I needed, plus many gift certificates to Jesse's health food store where I needed to purchase my supplements.

I was overwhelmed by God's grace and mercy on our lives, and Kenny and I were so thrilled that our children were seeing this firsthand. Moreover, I was told a few days later that because I had a long road ahead of me and because there were so many people asking how they could help, an account had been set up for us at church. Any time we didn't have the money to purchase my supplements, buy the groceries we needed, or pay for my nutritionist appointments, we were to call the church. There was money in an account just for us. It was a very humbling experience, I can assure you, but God supplied all of our needs through that account and many other sources, as well.

While basking in the "glow" of all that God was doing, it came time for me to return to the surgeon for my first follow-up appointment. I am probably the most nonconfrontational person you will ever meet, so I was truly dreading his reaction to my canceling the oncology appointment and choosing nutrition over conventional medical treatment.

The appointment started out very well. The surgeon was pleased with my healing progress, but he quickly cut to the chase. He wanted to know how my appointment went with the oncologist. When I told him that I had canceled the appointment and was pursuing nutrition instead, his eyes welled up with tears.

He said, "Sweet girl, do you realize how serious this is? Your cancer is so aggressive that this truly is the best option you have. You cannot mess around with this. I know you have little ones. I don't want you to risk your life and leave your young children without their mother."

Oh, dear. I would have been much better off if he had become angry and yelled at me, but he was so sincere in his concern for my children that I started crying too. I explained to him that I was a Christian and that I knew beyond any doubt that God was leading me down this path. I didn't know much about it, but I knew that I had to do it. I told him that I was so appreciative of his concern for me and my family, and I looked forward to future appointments when he could see how well I was doing.

There was nothing left to say, so he gave me a hug and wished me well. I was so shaken that I couldn't wait to get back to my car and take a minute to ask the Lord to please, please heal me and allow me to live to raise my children.

CHAPTER SIX

Support System

Now that my church friends and family had fully equipped us for "the battle plan," I began the 7-day organic juice fast. Jesse told me I was to juice three times a day. My vegetable juice was comprised of organic carrots, beets, celery, cucumbers, and parsley. I had that juice at mealtimes and drank as much purified water as I needed throughout the day. I also drank a detoxifying tea before I went to bed each night.

The juicing was a lot of work—cleaning the vegetables, cutting them, juicing them, cleaning the juicer, and then starting all over. My mom came up some days to help me. She was doing the same thing at home with my Dad. He was thrilled, I assure you. He did get to eat regular meals, but she gave him some juice each time she made it. My mom, Sandy, and my dear Kenny, followed the juice fast with me.

Jesse had warned me that the third day would probably be the hardest. He said that was usually the day when the body really started detoxifying. He was right. I woke up that morning extremely weak. I could get out of bed only to go to the bathroom. I had constant diarrhea and was starting to become concerned.

I called Jesse around lunchtime and told him how weak I was feeling. He said, "Terry, if you absolutely have to, you can eat an organic apple, but just one and only today." Fortunately, my Mom was with me that day, and she ran to the store and got both of us an organic apple—the biggest ones she could find. I felt so much better after I ate that and was able to get through the rest of the fast. Each day after that, I felt better and stronger.

At the conclusion of the fast, I began the 30-day program. Once again, I was not alone. Kenny, my mom, and Sandy followed the nutritional path with me. A wonderful friend from high school, Selena—my daughter Selena, was named after her—had some calcifications in her breasts that were being watched, which made her concerned; so she joined me on my diet as well. Each of these people encouraged me tremendously. I've never forgotten the sacrifices they made to join me on this unconventional and difficult journey.

If I told you that following this program were easy, I would be an outright liar. I remember opening the refrigerator on more than one occasion and just standing there sobbing. One day, Kenny caught me crying into the refrigerator and said, "Why are you crying, honey?"

I said, "I'm never going to get to eat anything good for the rest of my life." Mind you, I love fruits and vegetables. I had even made some pretty good bread. But the bottom line was: I love meat, especially red meat, and I have a sweet tooth as well. I was becoming very depressed about everything I *couldn't* have.

Kenny very wisely said, "Terry, don't think about the future. Just think about what you have to do *today* to reach your goal of being cancer-free. We have no idea what tomorrow may bring. We may get raptured, or you may get hit by a bus. "(That's the husband I know and love.)" God only gives us grace for today." That is so true! I started trying to think that way—taking one day at a time.

In spite of all the things God was doing and all of the encouragement of my family and friends, Satan was attacking me left and right. Every morning I would wake up terrified. All of the "what ifs" would flood my mind, and I would immediately head for my Bible. Every day, God would give me some word of encouragement, either through His Word, something someone said to me on the phone, or an unexpected visit from a friend. By evening, I would feel very encouraged, but the next morning I would be plagued, once again, with fear.

I would timidly tell God every morning, "Here I am again, Lord, paralyzed with fear. I hope you aren't ashamed of my weakness. I'm trying so hard to trust you, and I know this is your plan, but I don't know anyone who has done this before, and I don't have anyone to compare notes with. I'm so thankful for the encouragement you have given me so far. Please be patient with me!"

Every day, He would meet me at my need. I remember, one evening, being especially troubled after a phone call from a concerned friend. When I got off the phone, I passed by the bathroom where Kenny was taking a shower. He was singing (in his amazing tenor voice), "Trust and obey, for there's no other way, to be happy in Jesus, but to trust and obey." Thank you, God. I needed that.

When Kenny got out of the shower, I told him about the phone call and asked if he remembered what he had been singing in the shower. He didn't remember, but God knew I needed to hear that song, and He put it in Kenny's heart to sing, just for me and just at the moment I was passing by the bathroom. God cares about every detail, and He wants to meet each of our needs.

One afternoon, as I was coming home from work, I knew I needed to buy several bottles of supplements. I needed around a hundred dollars' worth, and our bank account was empty. I couldn't bear the thought of calling the church, once again, even though I knew the money was there. When I arrived home and opened the mailbox, there was a money order from an anonymous donor for one hundred dollars. I jumped for joy!

God continued to meet our financial needs and give me daily encouragement, but the fear continued. Then, one day when I was probably three weeks into my 30-day plan, Sandy called and told me of someone she had heard about at her church who had followed the same path I was taking. He had had lung cancer but was now cancer-free. She told me she had asked him to give me a call, and he said he would be very happy to speak with me. I could not wait to talk to him.

When he called, we spoke for a long time. It was such an encouraging time for me. It was another tremendous blessing in my life. Before we hung up, he said, "Please, feel free to call me anytime, day or night. I will be happy to encourage you in any way that I can."

The next morning when I woke up, I was no longer afraid. I had turned the corner. God had given me the strength that I needed to fight this battle, and we were going to do it together. I still wasn't happy with the diet; I still cried into the refrigerator from time to time; but I knew God was using this to heal me and was never going to leave my side. He had given me family and friends who were going to pray for me and support me in every way. Because of our faith, we were going to "see the glory of God" (John 11:40, NIV), and He was going to do "exceedingly abundantly above all that we ask or think" (Ephesians 3:20, KJV).

I was armed and ready for battle. A couple of weeks later, I completed the 30-day program. Jesse ordered some cancer antigen tests, which are specific blood tests for cancer markers. The blood work was performed, and when the results came back, they showed that I was, *indeed*, cancer-free!

CHAPTER SEVEN

Trying New Things

As my family and I continued on the vegan diet, I tried to find new and interesting recipes. Jesse had a wonderful vegetarian chef at his health food store, but when I finally had the time and energy to sign up for some of his cooking classes, he was taking a break from them. I did buy a couple of vegetarian cookbooks, which helped. One of my biggest challenges was Kristen. She hated vegetables, so this diet was a bit of a limitation for her. I started buying non-dairy pizza made with soy cheese. It was really good. Kristen loved it until someone accidentally let it slip that she wasn't eating real cheese.

Jordan Wood was Kristen's best friend, and Jordan's mom, Pat, was one of my closest friends. She was always trying to get Kristen to try new food items when she was at their house—which was a lot! Kristen's diet, I'm embarrassed to say, was limited to grilled cheese, mac and cheese, chicken nuggets, and french fries. I could get her to eat a raw carrot every once in a while. Pat was able to get her to try a few new things. She called me one day and said, "You're not going to believe this, but Kristen just ate a hamburger. I know it's not a vegetable, but at least it's something new and different."

When she was a baby, Kristen would eat whatever baby food I gave her, but once she started eating regular food, she would literally vomit if I tried to make her eat something she didn't want, which was typically any type of vegetable. I was so concerned that every time I visited the pediatrician's office, I would ask him what I could do to get her to eat vegetables without throwing them back up. He told me not to worry about it. Just let her eat what she would eat. He said the more you try to force her, the bigger her chances of developing an eating disorder, but it seemed apparent to me that she already had an eating disorder. I probably should have changed pediatricians, but not knowing where else to turn, I took his advice.

To make a long story short, it was years before Kristen learned to eat vegetables, and in the meantime I basically made separate meals for her. Kenny and Selena, on the other hand, were willing to try anything and never complained when I sprang something new on them. Well … almost never.

I mentioned before that I love red meat. I had been missing beef so much that when I came across a recipe for tofu meatloaf, I had to try it. Jesse was constantly trying to get me to try things that were totally foreign to me. He told me that tofu was a wonderful source of protein, and I needed to incorporate it into my diet. He said the nice thing about tofu is that it takes on the flavor of whatever you cook with it. Looking back, I probably should have tried introducing tofu in bits and pieces instead of making a whole loaf of it, but ...

That tofu meatloaf smelled so good, and from the outside it actually looked just like regular meatloaf. All of us were drawn to the smell of it. Since the beginning of my juice fast, months earlier, Kenny, Selena, and I had not eaten any meat, and we were interested in seeing if this was going to be a good substitute.

I put some on everybody's plate with Kristen being the obvious exception. Kenny, Selena, and I bravely took a bite of it. I immediately spit it into my napkin. Kenny and Selena rapidly followed suit. They were both so glad I spit first, because they didn't want to discourage me.

When I declared that tofu meatloaf was the most awful stuff I had ever put in my mouth, they agreed wholeheartedly. I'm sure Kristen was silently congratulating herself on her wise decision as she heartily ate macaroni and cheese. Tears came to my eyes. I was so sad. How could something that smelled so good (and cost so much), taste so bad? I decided to just throw it in the garbage, but Kenny stopped me and said, "No, don't throw it away. Feed it to Pooch for the next few days. She'll eat it."

Pooch was the Rottweiler/Shepherd mix that had knocked me down in the yard a couple of years earlier. She would eat anything—literally, anything: dirt, rocks, Christmas lightbulbs. I went out in the yard one day to fill her water bowl and strolled past a pile of multicolored poo comprised of red, green, and blue glass. I quickly realized that she had been eating the Christmas lights, which Kenny had put in the bushes. How she didn't die from that, I will never know.

Of course, it made perfect sense to feed the tofu meatloaf to Pooch. She would love it. She would probably love it even more than she loved rocks and Christmas lights. I heaped some in her bowl and brought her in the house for dinner. She trotted over to her bowl, took a sniff, and swiftly trotted away. "Wait a minute, Pooch, come back here," I said as I tried to coax her to take a bite. She wouldn't even taste it. Smart dog. At least I had tried. In the garbage it went.

Another thing Jesse tried to shove down my throat—I mean, encouraged me to try—was seaweed. One thing I did not miss on my new diet was seafood. I couldn't stand the taste of fish. Since I have a strong aversion to the taste of the ocean, why would I voluntarily *eat its weeds?* They float around in its water 24/7 soaking up that fishy taste that I detest. I tried seaweed once—never again.

During my 30-day plan I was introduced to so many unusual supplements that my gag reflex became very powerful. First thing in the morning, I drank this powdered supplement called "Nature's Blessing." It looked like green dirt. When I mixed it with water, I was reminded of the mud pies my little girlfriend and I would make in her backyard when we were four or five years old. Mind you, we never ate those mud pies; but if we had, I'm sure they would have tasted just like Nature's Blessing.

After I gagged the green dirt drink down, I drank four ounces of aloe juice. When I was growing up, we always had an aloe plant in our yard. Aloe is a miraculous healing agent for any kind of burns—kitchen burns, sunburns, you name it. My mom would go out and cut one of the leaves off of the aloe plant. She would cut the thorns off its sides and peel back the outside to reveal a green pulp that was covered with slime. She would take that slime and rub it on the burn. If we were sunburned, we would get covered with it. It smelled awful, but it really took the heat and the pain away.

Well, another word for aloe juice is "aloe slime," and I had to drink four ounces of that every morning after the Nature's Blessing. It tasted just like it smelled. I told Jesse the only way I could get that aloe down was to put it in grapefruit juice and hold my nose. He told me it was really important to take it straight to get all of the benefits. I told him it was really important for me to *get it down* if I was to get ANY of its benefits, and that was the only way I could do it.

Poor guy. I don't know how he put up with me, but I know I wasn't the only one that had a hard time with some of those supplements. I'm sure you can understand why my gag reflex kept getting stronger and stronger every day.

I also had to take a handful of supplements morning, noon, and night. I got to a point where I could only take one pill at a time because I gagged so easily. I had to get up pretty early in the morning to get all of my supplements taken before I had to leave for work.

I have to admit, however, that even though I was choking down some really horrid stuff, I never felt better in my life. People that knew I had been battling cancer could not believe how healthy I looked. People I didn't even know would tell me that my skin glowed and ask me what I did to look so healthy. I was so thankful that I wasn't sick during any of my natural treatment, except for the weakness and diarrhea that I had on the third day of my juice fast, and I was so thankful (for Kristen's sake especially) that I didn't lose my hair.

Looking back on the day we told the girls that I had cancer, I began to understand why Kristen became so upset about the possibility of me losing my hair. Kristen is now 24, and she's a great believer in the Bible verse that tell us a woman's hair is her glory" (see 1 Corinthians 5: 11:15), and she knows that a bad hair day can potentially be a "horrible, no good, very bad day." She rarely goes out the door unless her hair has been well taken care of: washed, blown dry, flat-ironed, and whatever else she needs to do to make it gorgeous.

Don't get me wrong; she doesn't idolize her hair, but she does make sure it is clean and looks beautiful. Now I understand why, even as a child, the thought of her mom losing her hair and wearing a wig was traumatizing.

Over the year following my surgery, I did a lot of research and changed more things than just my diet. Jesse told me I needed to get rid of all the chemicals and toxins in my house. My friend Dana, who had introduced me to Jesse and who also became one of my closest friends, introduced me to the Melaleuca Company. Melaleuca is a network marketing company that sells high-quality vitamins and chemical-free, non-toxic cleaning products, makeup, soaps, lotions, shampoo, etc. I began using their products and got rid of all of the chemicals in my house.

We had an exterminator for many years who came monthly to spray the yard and the inside of the house for bugs, fleas, etc. We had to explain to him that we could no longer use his services because of my health issues. That wasn't easy, because he had become a good friend.

My sister Donna, is a hairdresser. She had been coloring my hair for years—not because I had very much gray hair, but just because it was fun. I stopped coloring my hair or painting my fingernails and toenails. It is amazing how many chemicals our bodies ingest simply due to vanity.

I also stopped using antiperspirant deodorant. Antiperspirants and some deodorants use aluminum to hinder perspiration. Aluminum is highly toxic and is considered a carcinogen. When you use antiperspirant, you are placing a highly toxic carcinogen right on your lymph glands on a daily basis. I began using a natural deodorant from either the health food store or Melaleuca. Today, Arm and Hammer makes a wonderful natural deodorant that my husband and I both use. You may not be aware of this, but men can get breast cancer, too.

Another important principle Jesse introduced to me was to always stay as close to nature as possible. Because of this, I only eat butter, not margarine. Eating margarine is akin to eating plastic. It doesn't digest, but it does stick to the walls of your arteries. I also never ingest artificial sweeteners of any kind. If I'm going to indulge in something sweet, it is going to be made with real sugar. Artificial sweeteners are also highly toxic and carcinogenic. Do yourself a favor and stay away from them.

Typically, the only salt I use is iodized sea salt. It is so much healthier than regular salt, and it is an easy dietary change that will improve your health. Your taste buds won't know the difference. I have found one exception to this. If I use sea salt when I'm cooking lima beans, they taste fishy to me. Strange, I know, but because of my sensitive palate, I do have a container of regular iodized salt that I use only when I'm cooking lima beans. I also use it on the rare occasions that I'm making homemade ice cream. It works just as well as rock salt in keeping the ice cold when churning homemade ice cream, and it is so much cheaper.

I rarely drink anything but purified water. Once you get away from caffeine, carbonation, and sugary drinks, you don't crave them. I have come to realize that water is really the only drink that quenches my thirst.

CHAPTER EIGHT

Church Family and Friends

Another very healthy aspect of my life that helped me keep my perspective and my sanity, as well as creating many beautiful memories for me and my family, was the fellowship of my church and my dear friends. Looking back, these memories comprised most of the "bright spots" in my life during my cancer ordeal. Cornerstone's leadership came up with the most awesome ideas for church fellowships.

Cornerstone had a membership of about 300–400, I would estimate. To some that would be a big church and to others that would be a small church. Because of all the time we spent together, Cornerstone had a small church feel.

We had many additional events besides the typical Sunday morning Sunday School and church service, and the Wednesday night Bible study and choir practice. Sometimes on Sunday nights during the summer, our church family would go to a nearby park that had a beautiful pool and picnic area. The moms and most of the younger children would swim and play in the pool, and the husbands and the older children would play ball. We grilled hamburgers and hot dogs and had coleslaw and potato salad, along with lots of desserts, of course. We're Baptists so FOOD always goes with FELLOWSHIP. That's the law! ☺

For Thanksgiving each year, we had a full-blown Thanksgiving meal on the Tuesday night before Thanksgiving. The church would supply the turkey and ham, and the rest of us would bring all the sides and desserts. After the meal, Pastor Bill would take a few moments to turn our hearts toward all the blessings God had given us during the year, and because thankfulness is such an important facet of our Christianity, it was a wonderful precursor to our family Thanksgiving celebrations.

The women's ministry was led by some amazingly creative women. One night each month, we had craft night. A fairly large group of us would spend a few hours making a decoration for an upcoming holiday or simply something beautiful for our homes. We'd have some cookies or brownies to munch on and some fun opportunities to get to know each other better as we worked on our projects together.

One of the most awesome events the women's ministry sponsored each year, prior to Christmas, was a Saturday affair where the children could make Christmas ornaments, decorations, and candles. There was a small fee (five dollars per child, I think). We always brought our next-door neighbor with us. Kyesha, Selena, and Kristen looked forward to this enjoyable day each year, and so did I. It was a great outreach and amazing fun.

There were ten or more stations set up in the fellowship hall. The children would make their way around each station, making their project and enjoying their friends. At the end, there were cookies and drinks to enjoy before the kids got to go home and present all their goodies to their families. Our women's ministry team came up with the most adorable ideas for ornaments and decorations, and the children actually learned how to make candles. It was truly awesome. We still put those ornaments on our Christmas tree each year.

For our annual Christmas program, we celebrated with "Carols and Chaos," and that's exactly what it was. We sang carols, had soloists sing or play instruments, performed skits, laughed a whole lot, and then had refreshments, of course. One year, we divided the audience into 12 sections and acted out the 12 days of Christmas. Every time it came to "your" day, your section had to jump out of your seats and perform your day's description. I woke up the next morning feeling like I had been on a deep-knee-bend marathon. Ouch! But we were all laughing so hysterically watching everybody do their silly moves, we didn't realize we were exercising.

We also had a talent show night with singing, skits, instrumentalists, and dancing. We had a man in our church that sounded just like Elvis Presley, so he performed some Elvis songs. One wife sang a beautiful love song to her husband. The pastor's wife, Allyson, sang a really funny song to Pastor Bill. We had a group of ladies who sang and danced "I Heard It Through the Grapevine" dressed as California Raisins (I was one of them). There were many other performances and all ages participated. We had a blast!

Every Easter we had a passion play, complete with full choir and drama, including the crucifixion. It was powerful.

We always had very special events for Mother's Day and Father's Day. Every year the women's ministry planned a mother/daughter banquet for the Saturday of Mother's Day weekend. The sanctuary would be transformed into an elegantly decorated banquet hall, and the tables would be set so beautifully. Each year there was a different theme.

One year the theme was a "Wedding Dress Fashion Show." All the ladies were encouraged to pull their wedding dresses out of storage and model them, if they could. If not, they were encouraged to find someone who could. We saw some beautiful wedding dresses from years gone by (some were many, many years gone by!), and Kenny and I sang a wedding song duet at the end of the fashion show before dinner. It was a lovely day!

Another year, the theme for the mother/daughter banquet was "Quilts." All the ladies were encouraged to bring and display a quilt that they had made or that had been given to them or passed down in their family. I never realized we had so many quilters in our church. The sanctuary was filled that day with some of the most beautiful quilts I had ever seen. I decided I wanted to learn to quilt.

At the end of the banquet, a beautiful quilted wall hanging was raffled off. I had already fallen in love with it, and I wanted to win that quilt so bad. But I didn't, so I found out who made it and asked her to teach me to quilt.

When I approached Linda Bethune to ask if she could teach me how to make that quilted wall hanging, she said that it involved a lot of different techniques and wasn't really a starter quilt. I just couldn't take "no" for an answer; I wanted that quilt, so she said she would be happy to teach me. A couple of my other friends, who had already done some quilting, wanted to join us, so Linda, Pat Wood (Jordan's mom), Natalie Lyons (another dear friend), and I began meeting once a week to quilt.

We had such a wonderful time quilting and talking about our kids and happenings at church. We built a strong bond during those evenings together. I ended up making a quilt identical to the one that was raffled at the banquet, and it is proudly displayed in my family room to this day. I went on to make several other quilts for my daughters and family members. Those quilting times were such wonderful opportunities to build on my friendships with these ladies.

Natalie and I had never really had the opportunity to get to know each other until about a year before my cancer diagnosis. Her husband, Joe, had been previously diagnosed with a rare form of brain cancer, and they were going through a very tumultuous time with all the information that the doctors were throwing at them. I happened to see her sitting alone on a bench at our youth facility one evening, looking extremely forlorn.

Although I'm extremely shy and it is totally out of my comfort zone to approach someone I barely know, I felt compelled to sit down next to her and ask if she was all right. She just opened up (later I would find out that that was totally contrary to her personality, too), and I just listened. A strong friendship was initiated. We began walking and praying together a couple of nights a week, talking about our fears, our families, and what the Lord was doing in our lives. Joe had brain surgery, but due to the rare form of brain cancer he had, it took a miraculous touch from God to bring him to healing.

Pat and I became dear friends when our children were in preschool together. Kristen and Jordan hit if off immediately at 18 months old and became inseparable. They wanted to be together every waking moment, so Pat and I spent a lot of time together. In a lot of ways, Pat and I are polar opposites. I'm *slightly* obsessive-compulsive and extremely organized. She is very laid back, easygoing, and flies through life by the seat of her pants. We admire each other's abilities and strengths but enjoy teasing each other about our stark differences.

Dana, the one who introduced me to the nutritionist, became my biggest cheerleader. She knew firsthand about God's healing touch through nutrition. She provided a wealth of information and a lifeline for me. She was the single mom of three small children when she became completely bedridden for months with chronic fatigue syndrome. She overcame her illness through nutrition, and she was a huge blessing to me as I struggled through my 7-day fast, the 30-day plan, and into the following years.

Dana and Kenny share the same birthday and a lot of personality traits. They both make me laugh, but Dana makes me laugh so hard my face hurts for hours afterward. She does the zaniest things. I honestly don't know where she comes up with the stuff that she does, but she is hysterically funny, and since laughter is the best medicine, she was one of my best healing agents.

God lavished me with support from my precious family, my wonderful church, and my dear friends. He met my every need—physical, emotional, spiritual, and social.

CHAPTER NINE

Dad's Cancer Confession

Not long after my surgery, my dad informed my family that he had been diagnosed with cancer in the lymph glands on the right side of his neck *three years earlier*. He knew he wasn't going to subject himself to treatment, and because he didn't want us pressuring him to do so, he decided to keep it to himself.

Several years before this diagnosis, my dad had undergone surgery for a tumor on the underside of his tongue, which was determined to be squamous cell carcinoma, a type of skin cancer. By this time, my dad had been battling skin cancer for many years.

I explained previously that my dad was a smoker. He also chewed tobacco for many years. Both of these contributed to the cancer in his mouth. When he had the squamous cell tumor removed, we were so grateful that they did not have to remove any of his tongue. His doctor decided to treat him with radiation therapy.

My dad ended up losing all of his teeth, and his jaw bone was terribly damaged from the radiation.

After that, he was fitted for dentures. Due to his damaged jaw bone, the dentures were so uncomfortable that he couldn't wear them to eat, which is why he needed them, of course. You can imagine how miserable he felt.

I am fully aware that, over the years, medical research has improved the effectiveness of radiation therapy and chemotherapy. I believe the survival rate is much better now than it was twenty to thirty years ago, at least I hope so. In my opinion, though, the radiation therapy my dad received sent the cancer packing, but not out of his body—just to a new and more dangerous location: the lymph glands in his neck. From there it spread throughout his body.

By the time he told us about the cancer in his neck, he was beginning to have severe headaches because the cancer had metastasized to his brain. He also began blacking out. This happened one time as he and my mom were heading up to West Palm Beach from Miami. Fortunately, he felt it coming and was able to pull over to the side of the road before passing out completely over the steering wheel.

My mom immediately got out of the car and waved the next vehicle down that came into view. It was an RV driven by an older man. His wife was with him. They had a cell phone, which was not common at this time, and they were able to contact 911.

The hospital was only a few blocks away, and when the ambulance arrived there, my dad was seen almost immediately. After checking him thoroughly, the hospital physicians said there was nothing they could do for him, so they released dad with the admonition that he should stop driving. That went over like a lead balloon.

In the first chapter of this book, I mentioned that I was raised in a Christian home. I should have specified that it was a Christian home due solely to my mom's influence. My dad would attend church on Sunday morning, sleep through most of it, and go home. Although he said he accepted Jesus as his Savior as a teenager, there was never any real evidence of his salvation. He never complained about our involvement in church and never tried to hinder my mom or any of his children from church activities. He was even happy to send me to a Christian school and a Christian college, even though I know it was a financial hardship for him to do so.

I chose to attend a Christian college in Tennessee. For reasons initially unclear to me, my father was not happy with my selection. I couldn't understand why, because the college was in the town where he grew up, and we visited his aunt and uncle there every summer while I was growing up. We all loved it there, and I thought he would be thrilled that I chose that location.

It would be years later, after I graduated, before Dad let me know the basis for his feelings. While my dad was a young adult, his best friend had a gas station in that town. My father worked with him from time to time when he needed to make a little extra money or just when he wanted to hang out with his buddy. Back then, you could run a tab for your gas purchases if the owner of the station knew you and felt comfortable giving you that privilege. You could then pay your bill at the end of the month.

The pastor of a large Baptist church, who was also the president of the college that I would later attend, purchased his gas at my dad's friend's station and ran up a very large tab. He then refused to pay it. My dad became so infuriated that this very prominent pastor claimed to be a Christian but had no regard for the welfare of my dad's friend or his gas station.

That pastor's poor testimony turned my dad off to Christianity completely; he was still the pastor of the church and the president of the college when I began my college studies. Needless to say, that situation ate at my dad the whole time I was in college. He was so glad when my graduation was over, and he never set foot on that campus again. Now, years later, as my dad's health declined, we all became increasingly concerned for his spiritual welfare.

CHAPTER TEN

My Dad's Salvation

Not long after my dad passed out while he was driving, he passed out again at home and was taken by ambulance to the hospital. This time they admitted him to run some tests. Since this was his second trip to the hospital within a very short period of time, my brother-in-law, Ronnie, asked my family if we would mind if he talked to my dad about his spiritual condition. We were all thrilled for Ronnie to do that. We prayed with him before he went in to talk to my dad and continued praying during the time that they were together. I will let Ronnie tell you what transpired:

Hal was back in the hospital, and the prognosis was grim. We were close. He treated me more like a son than a son-in-law, and my heart was saddened at the thought of losing him; but my greatest concern and fear was about his standing with God. Would Hal go to heaven when he died or be lost for eternity? He was a good man. Even though he tried to project the tough and gruff persona, he had a heart of gold and was a dedicated family man. However, I knew that according to the Bible, God's holy Word, no amount of good works or personal merit would earn him a place in heaven. My heart was burdened. I had to know for sure. So, I asked if I could go in to see him alone.

I walked into the room, and after just a couple of minutes of general chit chat, I cut to the chase and said, "Hal, I want to ask you a question, and I want you to be straight with me. I need the truth. When you depart this world, are you absolutely certain that you will go to heaven to be with God?"

He answered in his typical authoritative style. "Now, Ronnie, I am not into that religious stuff. I go to church with the family, but it is not for me."

"Why not?"

"Well, I'll tell you. When I was a young adult living in Tennessee, I started faithfully attending a church until I found out that the young pastor was a drunk and a hypocrite. He would sneak around drinking moonshine. After I heard about that, I had no use for church or religion. Now, I'm glad you and Sandy go to church, but it is not for me."

As I silently prayed for help, God emboldened me to reply, "Hal, you listen to me! That preacher was wrong, and someday he will have to answer to God for his actions; but what does that have to do with you?"

"Now, Ronnie …"

"No, you listen to me! You have allowed this so-called 'preacher' to cheat you out of enjoying church and knowing God for all these years, and now you are going to allow him to send you to hell? It is not like you to let someone take advantage of you! That man will have to answer for his choices, but you have to answer for yours. Now, just listen to me for a minute.

"Heaven—eternal life and the privilege of living with God forever—is a free gift. The Bible says, 'The gift of God is eternal life through Christ Jesus our Lord.' And because heaven is a genuine gift, it is not earned or deserved. No amount of personal effort, good works, or religious deeds can earn a place in heaven for you. In Ephesians 2:8-9 we are taught, 'For by grace you have been saved through faith, and that not of yourselves; it is the gift of God, not of works, lest anyone should boast' (NKJV).

"Because we are all sinners, we cannot earn our way to heaven. Romans 3:23 teaches,

'For all have sinned and fall short of the glory of God' (NKJV). Sin is anything that is displeasing to God and includes such things like lying, cheating, and stealing. Because of sin, man cannot save himself. To save ourselves by good works, we would have to be perfect. Matthew 5:48 teaches, 'Therefore, you shall be perfect, just as your Father in heaven is perfect' (NKJV). We are not perfect, because we all are sinners; therefore, we are disqualified from saving ourselves.

"However, in spite of our sins, God loves us and does not want to punish us. The Bible says in 1 John 4:8 that 'God is love.' But the same Bible that tells us that God loves us also tells us that God is just and, therefore, must punish sin. Exodus 34:7 says that He will not clear the guilty. This appears to have created a dilemma. On one hand, God loves us and does not want to punish us; but on the other hand, He is just and must punish sin. God solved this problem for us in the person of Jesus Christ.

"Jesus is God who came from heaven to earth. Jesus lived a perfect, sinless life. He died on the cross to pay the penalty for our sins, and He rose from the grave to purchase a place in heaven for us.

"'All we like sheep have gone astray; we have turned, every one, to his own way; and the Lord has laid on Him the iniquity of us all' (Isaiah 53:6, NKJV).

"Jesus paid the penalty for our sins and now offers you eternal life as a free gift. This gift is received by faith. Saving faith is trusting in Jesus Christ, alone, for eternal life. This means trusting in Christ and what He did on the cross, rather than what you may have tried to do to get into heaven. It means trusting in Jesus' death, burial, and resurrection as the sufficient and only payment for your sins.

"Acts 16:31 says, 'Believe on the Lord Jesus Christ, and you will be saved' (NKJV).

"John 3:16 says, 'For God so loved the world that He gave His only begotten Son, that whoever believes in Him should not perish but have everlasting life' (NKJV)"

I then asked, "Hal, Jesus loves you, and He died for your sins so that you could go to heaven. Do you understand this?"

He answered quietly, "Yes."

I continued, "Would you like to receive His free gift of eternal life?"

I was unsure as to what he might answer, but I was relieved and overjoyed when he said, "Yes, I would."

"Great! We can pray right now, and you can ask Him to be your Lord and Savior. Hal, if you are sincere about trusting Christ as your Savior, pray this prayer with me. You can pray audibly or silently: 'Lord Jesus, thank You for Your free gift of eternal life. I know I am a sinner and do not deserve eternal life; but because You loved me, You died for me, and then rose from the grave to purchase a place in heaven for me. I now trust in You, alone, for eternal life and repent of my sin. Please take control of my life. Thank You.'"

Hal prayed silently with me, and at the end I asked, "Did you pray?"

He answered, "Yes!"

"Hal, once again, I have to know the truth. Did you pray to appease me or were you sincere?"

"No, I was sincere, I meant it."

I was filled with emotion, but was able to say, "Praise God!"

I now knew with confidence, whether Hal received God's healing touch while he was still on earth or if He received the ultimate healing when God took him home to heaven—and in spite of Satan's attempts to discourage and disillusion him by the actions of others—Hal made the decision that would someday allow him to be in the presence of His Savior, Jesus Christ, for eternity!

There was an obvious change in my father's behavior after that day. Once he was released from the hospital, he wanted to be in church every Sunday morning, and his gruff personality took on a softer and gentler demeanor. He kept hoping that God would heal him so that he would have a chance to do something in his earthly life that would bring glory to God. He wanted to have the opportunity to tell others not to make the mistakes that he made. He didn't want anyone else to waste his/her life as he felt that he had.

As the cancer progressed, my dad began having heart problems. He was given a pacemaker which seemed to help for a period of time. He lost weight steadily. I remember his headaches becoming so excruciating that he would lie flat on his back on the carpeted living room floor. I don't know what kind of relief that gave him, but when he was in a lot of pain, that is where we found him. He never wanted anyone to do anything for him, and he never complained.

My mom had already started juicing for him before she knew about the cancer, but once she knew, she juiced for him all the time. My dad consulted with Jesse, and Jesse tried to put him on the same regimen that I was on. He did what Jesse told him for the most part, but he also did a lot of what he wanted to do. The cancer was so advanced by the time my dad told us about it that I don't think it would have mattered how strict he was. I do believe, though, that his quality of life was better than it would have been if he had not been trying to follow Jesse's plan.

I remember Jesse telling me that most cancers were curable through nutrition, but once it is in the liver and/or pancreas, it is very difficult to fight, no matter the treatment. My dad's abdomen was full of tumors, so I believe it was also in his liver and possibly his pancreas.

Eight days before he died, my dad had a bleed out, which means he was bleeding profusely from his rectum. He was rushed to the hospital by ambulance and wasn't expected to live more than a few hours. He was transferred to the hospice unit. I can't sing enough praises for the hospice nurses and doctors. They were amazing to both my dad and my family, always letting us know what to expect—honestly, yet gently.

About five days after the bleed out, my dad perked up and seemed to make an incredible turnaround. We wondered if God was healing him. The hospice nurses said anything was possible (which we already knew), but many times hospice patients seemed to get better right before the end. That was the case with my father.

I remember several times, during those final days, my father saying he was hoping God would heal him. He felt that he wasted his life by not doing anything for God, and he wanted God to give him a chance to do something for Him. He did not want to get to heaven and not have any crowns to give back to Jesus. We were happy he felt that way and did not know what God's plan was, but we were comforted knowing he was going to heaven when his time came to die.

On the evening following his seeming improvement, Dad slipped into a coma. My sisters, my mom, and I gathered around his bed and sang hymns to him. The rest of our family joined us or relieved us from time to time, and friends visited. The next morning my sister Donna and I were standing one on each side of my dad's bed. We began to reminisce. I said how much I loved Dad's hands. He had very masculine hands, and he could fix *anything* with them. We were also both commenting on how handsome we both thought he was as we were growing up.

Donna, being the oldest, remembered when my dad was in the Air Force and said he always looked so handsome in his uniform. I mentioned how my mom had told me that on many occasions. Sandy walked in the room about that time. Not having any idea what we had been talking about, she came over to kiss dad on the cheek and said, "Look, Dad has a huge tear coming down his face!" Donna and I felt that he had been listening to us as we reminisced about him. We were happy that he may have heard all the complimentary things we said about him.

A few hours later, while Dad was still in a coma, he sat up in the bed and reached up toward the ceiling. At that moment, we thought he was leaving us, and I remember telling him, "If you see Jesus, Daddy, just run to meet him! We'll be okay." He stayed in that position for a few more seconds and then quietly lay back down. That was the last movement he made.

Several hours later, on the morning of April 28, 1997, at 1:07 a.m., Jesus came to carry my dad into perfect health and the glorious splendor of heaven while my mom, Donna, Sandy, and I looked on. It was a very peaceful transition—no more tears, no more pain, no more suffering. After a four-year battle with cancer, Dad was finally home.

CHAPTER ELEVEN

Another Miracle

My dad's battle with cancer ended less than a year after my breast cancer surgery. During that year, I was to continue following up with my surgeon every three months. I was supposed to have a mammogram three months after my surgery, but I could only imagine how painful that would be, and I didn't do it.

My sweet surgeon officially retired when I was about three months out from surgery. He recommended me to another surgeon who was one of the top rated surgeons in Coral Springs. The new surgeon appeared to be about my age and was very knowledgeable. He was, of course, very skeptical of my decision to pursue nutrition as my treatment, but he was still willing to follow up with me. He did advise that I would absolutely have to have a mammogram no later than 12 months after my surgery.

When my one-year reprieve was up, less than two months after my father's death, I dutifully scheduled the mammogram. When I was taken in for the procedure, I tearfully explained to the technician how fearful I was of the pain I expected to endure. She assured me she would be very careful and as gentle as she possibly could be. I was surprised to find that it wasn't any worse than the mammograms I had experienced pre-surgery. Unfortunately, days later, I received results that showed a suspicious area once again in my right breast.

I immediately conferred with my new surgeon. While in his office, he showed me the films. The suspicious area or "lesion" was very small and looked exactly like the tiny used blade you break off the end of an X-Acto knife. It was the same shape and size. He explained that we could not waste any time finding out exactly what this was. He said that it was possible it could be scar tissue, but we couldn't take any chances. He wanted to schedule a stereotactic biopsy at the hospital. He then explained what would be entailed and how he expected things to go.

First, once I was admitted to the hospital, a mammogram would be done; once the lesion was located, a needle would be inserted into my breast at the exact location of the lesion. Then I would be prepped for the stereotactic biopsy. The surgeon would then be able, during the procedure, to go directly to the lesion, remove it, and biopsy it, right then and there. If the tissue was malignant, due to the aggressive nature of my previous breast cancer, the surgeon would proceed with a double mastectomy; and if the tissue was benign, he would close me up, and I would go home that day. The biopsy was scheduled, and I was to meet him at the hospital seven days later for the procedure.

I was stunned, of course, by all of the information that was coming at me so rapidly, but once he said "seven days," an idea immediately popped into my head, and I felt certain the Holy Spirit put it there. There are a lot of special numbers in the Bible that God uses over and over. One of the most common is the number seven. Seven is the number of perfection or completion. My mom has always been fascinated by the significance of these special numbers, especially the number seven.

When I realized that I had a full seven days until my surgery, I felt strongly impressed to do a seven-day fast. I began to pray about whether this was truly God's leading. He reassured me that it was and that He was going to remove this "lesion" during the fast.

Kenny and I were both excited. Once again I contacted my mom and Sandy, and they decided to join me in this seven-day fast—no surprises there. I know I mentioned earlier that Kenny, my mom, and Sandy all fasted with me on that initial seven-day juice fast, but I failed to mention that my mom kept fasting. She fasted for a total of 57 days! Jesse finally told me to tell her to STOP; even Jesus only fasted for *40 days*.

What an amazing mother I have! She wanted God's healing on my life so intensely, she was willing to fast and pray for nearly two months for me. I know that God's healing was a direct result of not only my mother's faithfulness, but also of the many people praying for me all over the country, and even some in other parts of the world.

Kenny was not able to join us on this second fast. Due to the very physical nature of his job, he had a difficult time with the first fast, and we decided it wasn't a good idea for him to do that again. Because he was following me on my diet, he had lost a lot of weight, almost too much, and needed to incorporate more protein in his diet in order to maintain his weight. He did a lot of weight lifting and was very faithful to exercise, but he started having an unusual amount of pain in his joints and muscles. Due to these new developments, he began modifying the diet in order to address these issues.

My mom, Sandy, and I began the juice fast immediately, with great anticipation. I felt the Lord encouraging me every day to expect the lesion to be gone by the time I went back to the hospital. John 11:40 says, "Then Jesus said, 'Did I not tell you that if you believe, you will see the glory of God?'" (NIV). I was fully anticipating God showing up and displaying His glory.

My church called a special prayer meeting for me. The deacons (many churches call them "elders") and my other church friends, along with my family, met together the night before my scheduled surgery. I shared with them what I felt God had in store for us the next day.

My dear friend, Linda Hicks, shared a verse that she felt God gave her specifically for me that morning in her personal devotions. It was 2 Chronicles 20:17: "You will not have to fight this battle. Take up your positions; stand firm and see the deliverance the Lord will give you, ... Do not be afraid; do not be discouraged. Go out to face them tomorrow, and the Lord will be with you" (NIV).

Wow! I still get goose bumps and become teary-eyed every time I read that verse. That was just another incredible confirmation of what I felt the Lord told me six days earlier.

The deacons anointed my head with oil and laid hands on me in accordance with James 5:14-15: "Is any one of you sick? He should call the elders of the church to pray over him and anoint him with oil in the name of the Lord. And the prayer offered in faith will make the sick person well; the Lord will raise him up" (NIV).

One of the deacons started the prayer time, and whoever felt led to pray followed him. I was totally and completely bathed in prayer that night. What a sweet time of encouragement and confirmation! I was ready to get this show (of God's glory) on the road.

The next morning we arrived at the hospital and checked in. I remember signing the paperwork giving the surgeon permission to perform a double mastectomy if there were any malignancy. For a moment, an arrow of doubt pierced my heart. *"God, are you sure you have healed me?"* I began to feel overcome with anxiety, when I suddenly remembered the verse God had given Linda only 24 hours earlier. I did not have to fight this battle. Why? Because He already fought it for me. I was already healed.

Once again, there was a crowd of family and church friends waiting to pray with Kenny and me in the waiting room. My mammogram was delayed a few minutes, which was a wonderful opportunity for an extended prayer time. Minutes after we finished praying, a nurse came and whisked me away for the procedure. The technician explained in detail how this mammogram would be different.

My breast was going to be compressed for a long enough period of time for the technician to shoot the films, find the lesion, stick the needle directly in it, shoot more films to ensure the needle was, in fact, in the exact location, and then I would be able to relax. I was not happy with that news. It appeared that my breast could be stuck in a literal vise-grip for 30 minutes or more.

The technician began the mammogram. She called a nurse in to stay with me while she went to develop the films. It happened to be the nurse who had wheeled me back from the waiting room. She began asking me questions in an effort to distract me from the discomfort I was enduring.

She asked who all the people were in the waiting room, and I explained that some of them were my family, but my pastor and his wife were also there, along with many church friends. She began sharing with me that she had grown up in a Christian home but had gotten away from going to church. She was a single mom and was too busy to go to church, but lately she had really been missing it.

We talked about my cancer ordeal, and I shared what I had been doing and some of the wonderful things God had done for me during the past year. I told her that I believed God had already removed this lesion and that I felt certain the technician was not going to be able to find it. She was astonished. She hoped I was right and couldn't wait to see how this all turned out. She said if God healed me, she was going back to church.

By this time, I had been in the mammogram's clutches for over an hour. The nurse was literally holding me up because I was feeling so nauseated and weak from the discomfort as well as from my lack of eating for seven days. Having had nothing to drink since midnight the night before did not help either.

The technician finally returned. She released me from the compression and told me there was something wrong with the machine. She could not find the lesion on any of the films. I shot a quick glance at the nurse, who already had a huge smile across her face. The tech said my surgeon had been waiting in the operating room for me for over an hour and had been calling to find out what was going on. He instructed the technician to bring me and the films downstairs. He was going to find a doctor to perform an ultrasound and see if they could locate the spot that way. He was already prepped for surgery and didn't want to have to go through that process again.

The doctor who performed the ultrasound was very thorough. I told her she wasn't going to find the lesion because God had removed it. She just smiled. She was probably thinking, "This lady is a looney tune." She tried for a long time, but she could not find it. Finally, she called into the operating room and told the surgeon she had not been able to locate it.

He finally came and tried to find it himself because, you know, if you want something done right, you have to do it yourself. At least that's my motto. Just ask my family.

I told my surgeon that he wasn't going to find the lesion—that God had removed it. He very politely said, "Oh, it is there, and we will find it."

After searching for a good long while, he finally gave up. "We're just going to have to wait three months and do another mammogram." I said, "Okay, but it still won't be there because, I promise you, God has healed me." To which he replied, "We'll see."

My sweet nurse returned to wheel me back to the waiting room. She could hardly contain herself. We hugged and laughed and cried. We were both eager to see the looks on the faces of my family and friends who were waiting back in the waiting room.

When I arrived, they were expecting to see the doctor and to hear his report of the results of the biopsy and/or surgery. Instead here I was looking the same as I did when I left them two hours earlier.

"What happened?" Everybody wanted to know. "Was the biopsy benign?" Kenny asked. I said, "There was no biopsy. We never got past the mammogram. God has shown His glory and the lesion is gone."

There were shouts of praise and jubilation. We all stopped to pray and thank God for His mercy, grace, and healing touch. Then, we all went home thankful that we had seen God's glory firsthand that morning. Amen, praise the Lord, and HALLELUJAH!

CHAPTER TWELVE

Insecurity Issues

During the two years following my surgery, I struggled immensely with my deformity. I knew that Kenny loved me; that wasn't the problem. *I* didn't love me. I had always disliked my body, and now I was disfigured in addition to all the other things I had never accepted about myself.

Kenny, on the other hand, loved my body, including my deformity. It truly did not make a difference in the way he felt about me; but because of my insecurities, I never wanted him to see me naked. I always turned the lights out or hid in the bathroom when I changed clothes. Intimacy, in general, became very uncomfortable for me.

Kenny was understanding, comforting, and encouraging, but I could not get past the way I felt about myself. I honestly could not understand how he couldn't see how ugly I was.

From the moment I got married, I wanted to be the very best wife I could possibly be. I read all kinds of Christian books on marriage and understanding your mate. Kenny and I went to every Christian marriage conference that came to town. I knew the importance of communication and a strong sexual relationship in marriage. I realized that my insecurities were putting my husband and my marriage at risk.

I had read books about how men and women are totally different in their thought processes. I'm speaking in generalities here because there are exceptions to every rule, but for most men, sex confirms their masculinity. When a man is able to sexually fulfill his wife, he feels like a super hero. However, he can become totally devastated if he feels rejected by his wife.

A woman, on the other hand, thrives on compliments and thoughtful gestures. Although sex is a wonderful thing to a woman, it doesn't seem to have anything to do with her *identity*.

Men also need compliments and thoughtful gestures. As marriage partners, I believe we should not forget how to flirt with our spouses. It may sound juvenile, but it is a great way to reignite the flames that have been doused by years of stress, financial hardship, health issues, and all the other real-life, everyday problems that we have to face in life.

Having a playful and lighthearted attitude can bring some much needed relief when life becomes too solemn. Because I have a tendency to look at everything from a very serious perspective, this is a lesson I truly need to learn.

Following my surgery, Kenny never stopped the compliments and thoughtful gestures, but I was losing ground on making him feel like a super hero.

During the first two postsurgical years, I had been through *my* breast cancer battle, while simultaneously dealing with *my father's* cancer battle and his subsequent death. Before I had the opportunity to fully grieve my father's death, I was then unexpectedly confronted with the possibility of having another battle with breast cancer and possibly more disfigurement.

Needless to say, Kenny's needs got lost in all of that turmoil. Even though God was doing amazing things in the midst of all of these upheavals, I had lost sight of the importance of communication and intimacy in my marriage; even though our marriage wasn't totally devoid of communication and intimacy, we were definitely in a dangerous place. After all of the victories God had given us during those twenty-four months, Satan would have loved nothing more than to destroy our marriage and devastate our children.

Fortunately, Kenny and I were both committed to our marriage. Kenny knew all of the stress I was going through. He understood all of the emotions I was dealing with. He wasn't being selfish when he finally came to me and explained how helpless he felt and how lonely he was in our marriage. He was at the point of desperation. I loved him dearly and wanted to meet his needs, but I was so insecure I didn't know what to do to get past my personal pain, but I knew I had to do something.

Thankfully, a few days after Kenny and I had this conversation, I had my two year checkup with the surgeon. I had seen him a couple of times since the stereotactic biopsy went awry (or rather, God's way), and he continued to be surprised at how healthy I was. I enjoyed that thoroughly, of course. This time, Kenny went with me to my appointment. We were trying to make each other a priority and spend as much time with each other as possible.

When the surgeon pulled back my paper gown to do a breast exam, I winced. Sensing how uncomfortable I was, he asked, "Terry, how do you feel about the way you look?" I said, "I hate it!" He gently said, "That is obvious. Have you considered reconstruction?" I told him I had not because I was afraid that if I had implants, they would possibly keep a malignancy from showing up on a mammogram, or the surgery itself may cause the cancer to start growing again.

He said, "Terry, I do not believe that would happen, but let me ask you something. Would you rather live the rest of your life feeling the way you do about yourself—I expect that it might be causing some problems in your marriage—or would you rather take the risk and feel a whole lot better about yourself?"

I looked at Kenny and thought of how wonderfully he had taken care of me, through better or worse, and what an awesome husband and father he was. I thought of how much I longed to be the best wife to him that I could possibly be, so I said, "I'm willing to take the risk."

My surgeon referred me to a plastic surgeon. When I called to schedule the appointment, I was told that I needed a referral from my primary care physician. I called and spoke with the nurse who handled such referrals. She knew me well. She told me that she felt certain my insurance company would reject the referral. She said that she had tried on many occasions to get this same type of referral from this particular insurance company, and they always rejected it. I said, "But I've had breast cancer. This is not just a boob job. This is reconstruction after a mastectomy." She said she understood, and she would do the best she could.

I hung up the phone, and within less than five minutes, she called me back, and said, "I can't believe I'm telling you this, but I have your referral, Mrs. Hohenstein. You may pick it up at your convenience." I hadn't even had time to pray about it, but God took care of it for me. That seemed like a confirmation from Him that it was okay for me to go ahead with the surgery, and I did. It literally changed my life and revolutionized our marriage.

Shortly after my surgery, a law was passed that required insurance companies to cover breast reconstruction after a mastectomy at 100 percent. I was sorry that it wasn't in place when I had my surgery, but I was so thrilled for all those women who would come after me and that they would have the opportunity to feel whole again at no unnecessary expense to them.

I recommend to anyone reading this book that if there is something you don't like about your body and it is crippling you emotionally, if God gives you the opportunity to change it or fix it, *just do it.*

I believe the "Serenity Prayer" speaks to this situation perfectly: "God grant me the serenity to accept the things I cannot change, the courage to change the things I can, and the wisdom to know the difference."

To me, the most difficult part of that prayer is accepting the things I cannot change, but God is teaching me that He can work in me and enable me to accept those things if I give them to Him in prayer.

CHAPTER THIRTEEN
Life Goes On

A couple of years after my surgery, while working at Coral Springs Christian School, one of our school moms was diagnosed with ovarian cancer. She was a little older than I, but her two boys were very young. One was in kindergarten, and the other was in first or second grade. Someone told this mom, Elaine, about my cancer experience, and we began talking.

She decided to go with the conventional treatment that her doctor recommended, but she also incorporated a couple of the nutritional things that I had done. I felt sure the Lord was going to heal her because her husband and young boys needed her so much. But, as with most ovarian cancer patients, her cancer was well advanced by the time they found it, and the conventional cancer treatment and the few nutritional things she was doing weren't enough to ward off the cancer that was rapidly spreading throughout her body.

I brought a meal to her home one evening and had the opportunity to visit with her for a few minutes not long before her death. I kept hoping the Lord would turn things around and perform a miracle in her life, but she shared with me that God had given her a perfect peace about leaving her husband and children behind. She knew she was going to heaven and that God would provide for them. She was comforted in knowing that though they would be separated for a time, they would be together forever in heaven for eternity.

When she told me that, I knew that her healing was going to come in heaven and not on earth. I was so sad, and yet, at the same time, thankful that God had never given *me* that peace.

I couldn't understand why God chose to take her, and yet allowed me to be healed. I also couldn't understand why she didn't choose to jump headlong into the nutritional plan I followed, and possibly be healed as well, but I had to learn that God works in so many different ways.

He can heal people with nutrition; He can heal them with conventional treatment; He can heal them with an outright miracle, involving no treatment; and He can choose to take them home to the ultimate healing. It's not necessary for me to understand His ways or to impose my beliefs on anyone else. So if anyone asks me what my cancer treatment entailed, I'm happy to tell them. If they choose to do it, I'm glad to cheer them on. But if they don't, I ask the Lord to lead them into the plan that He has for them, because I know that He is the Great Physician, and His healing is not limited to any particular type of treatment.

I continued following Jesse's nutrition plan strictly and faithfully for nearly three years; then I "fell off the wagon" during a wonderful family vacation to the "Amish Country" in Lancaster County, Pennsylvania. The food there was amazing and, in retrospect, very healthy—lots of wonderful homegrown vegetables. My mouth is watering as I think about it. My downfall, though, was the Shoofly Pie. If you haven't heard of it, you are probably thinking, "What the heck is that?" That's exactly what I said, and after having absolutely no sugar for nearly three years, I wanted to be disinterested.

Even after I saw a piece of it, I wasn't that curious. It is made with a lot of molasses and just looks and smells very rich and strong. I finally gave in and made the mistake of tasting it. I didn't even like it at first. It is almost bitter. If you have ever tasted straight molasses, you probably understand what I mean. I think what did me in was the sugar. After abstaining completely from sugar for such a long period of time, just that tiny bite was all it took to reel me back in— probably like an alcoholic who hasn't had a drink in a long period of time and thinks he can handle it, only to find out that he can't. Well, that was me.

On our last day in Pennsylvania, we went into this cute bookstore that had a little café in it. It was a pretty big place, and we all kind of spread out looking at different things. Finally, when everybody was ready to leave, nobody knew where I was. They finally found me sitting in the back corner of the café trying to hide as I ate my last ever piece of Shoofly Pie! I think I gained ten pounds on that seven-day trip.

After our Amish adventure, I tried to be careful, but I didn't continue on Jesse's diet with the same amount of strictness. Although Jesse had told me plainly that I needed to make this diet my lifestyle, I had wondered from the outset how long I could do it. I know there are many people who have made the change permanently, but I have struggled with depression since my early teen years; I became very depressed over all the things I could not eat.

One thing that bothered me the most was social events. People would say, "I want to have you over for dinner, but I don't know what to cook for you." Or, "I would like to invite you to this party, but I don't know if there will be anything there that you can eat." Similarly, I would want to have someone over for dinner, but I would not know what to cook that I could eat and that my guests would enjoy. I finally returned to a more "normal" diet, although as I said before, I try to be wise.

Through the years, I have always prayed for guidance. There came a time when I knew I was going to have to cut out some of the supplements I was taking. I had to reach a reasonable compromise between my health and our family's finances. I feel that God has led me along a path that was right for me.

Sometime in the year 2001, six years after my doctor said he thought I may have some type of autoimmune disease, specifically multiple sclerosis, I started noticing that I was losing some of my hearing. I was referred to an ear, nose, and throat specialist (ENT).

On my initial visit, he asked a lot of questions about my history and did a thorough hearing exam. It was obvious that I had lost the ability to hear high-pitched sounds. Because of my breast cancer history, he wanted to send me for an MRI of the brain, specifically both inner ears. He didn't want to alarm me, but breast cancer sometimes metastasizes to the inner ear, and he just wanted to rule that out.

When the ENT received the MRI results, he called me back into his office. When he showed me the films, I saw several white spots on my brain. He said they were lesions. When I asked if it was cancer he said, "No, it is not, but I showed your films to the neurologist that shares this office, and he says that it is possible you have multiple sclerosis." I told him he was probably right, and I went on to explain the numbness in my right leg six years prior and the doctor's suspicions at that time.

We scheduled an appointment with the neurologist, and I went in for a consultation. He asked me if I had noticed certain changes over the past several years that would point to my having MS. One of the main alterations to my lifestyle was fatigue; yes, I realized that I had become more and more fatigued over the past several years. I had always worked full time, and it was getting harder and harder to work all day and then come home and accomplish everything that I needed to at home.

He also explained to me that numbness in the extremities, sensitivity to heat, loss of hearing, eye problems, bowel problems, bladder problems, motion sickness, and dizziness were just some of the things people experience with MS. I had been having problems in all of those areas, but they had been coming on gradually, and I was so busy, I didn't give them much thought.

He continued to explain more about MS, stating that it is an autoimmune disease that affects the nervous system. Without getting too technical, let me explain briefly that your nervous system is your body's electrical system, and the center of your nervous system is your spinal cord and brain. Your spinal cord has a protective covering called the myelin sheath. If you can picture an electrical wire, the protective outside covering of that wire is very similar to the myelin sheath. That protective covering keeps the electrical impulses moving along the wire without interruption. The myelin sheath does the same thing for your spinal cord.

With MS, your immune system, which normally fights for you, turns against you through some strange twist of events that nobody has been able to figure out. Your own cells begin eating away at the myelin sheath of your spinal cord. Once that cord is exposed, the electrical impulses that send messages throughout your body telling it how to respond to stimuli are interrupted. These exposed areas are called "lesions," and they can be found on both your spinal cord and in your brain.

Another word for lesions is "scars." The word "sclerosis" means scars, so simply put, multiple sclerosis means "multiple scars on your spinal cord and brain." MS patients have symptoms which vary according to both the anatomic location and the severity of the scars in their nervous system.

The neurologist also explained a little about the treatment and told me that patients, in general, had flu-like symptoms with the medication, and many times the treatment was about 30 percent effective in controlling the symptoms and the severity of an exacerbation or attack.

Because I had numerous symptoms, the neurologist decided to perform a spinal tap or lumbar puncture. This test would provide definitive answers. I had a few days before the spinal tap to think about what I would do if I were diagnosed with MS. It was a no-brainer for me. If I did, in fact, have multiple sclerosis, and if the medication—which is only effective 30 percent of the time—makes you feel like you have the flu, I would just have to go on a quest to find natural ways to deal with it.

The spinal tap was done, and the results were in. I had multiple sclerosis. I told the neurologist I wasn't interested in taking the medication. Once again, I prayed for God to guide me as to how I needed to treat this new illness.

CHAPTER FOURTEEN
Seeing an Oncologist

We had been living in West Palm Beach for at least a year when I was diagnosed with multiple sclerosis. I was working at The King's Academy, a wonderful Christian school where my daughters attended. I was the high school principal's secretary, and I had the privilege of working with wonderful staff, students, parents, and teachers; plus, I was with my children. What could be better?

During my time there, I became friends with Selena's P.E. teacher, Kelly Lord. She was a beautiful young lady with her own cancer story. Years earlier she had been diagnosed with Hodgkin's lymphoma in her chest wall. She agreed to the recommended treatment which was radiation therapy. The disease went into remission, but, unfortunately, Kelly was diagnosed with breast cancer a year or two later. She strongly believed the breast cancer was a direct result of the radiation therapy.

After already having dealt with the negative side effects of radiation and now seeing what she believed to be the consequences of that therapy, she told the doctors she had no interest in pursuing any of their recommendations. She too turned to nutrition and had great results.

Kelly began encouraging me to go to her oncologist. I strongly resisted. She kept telling me that her oncologist was a sweet Christian doctor who didn't put any pressure on her to change her course of treatment; she was just there to recommend the different tests that Kelly needed along the way to ensure that the cancer was in remission.

Because I had not had any cancer testing for a while, I finally decided to make an appointment with the oncologist. I liked her instantly. She had a very gentle, easy-going personality and showed a sincere interest in learning more about my treatment. She was especially eager to hear my story because her husband was experiencing some health problems, and a friend of theirs recently recommended some alternative (nutritional) treatments for him, which he was trying with great results.

When I gave her the details of my diagnosis, surgery, and postoperative recommendations, she said, "Let me make sure I have these dates right. You said your partial mastectomy and lymph dissection were performed in June 1996, and at that time the oncologist was suggesting stem cell replacement chemotherapy?" When I confirmed, she excused herself for a moment. She needed to check some records.

She came back a few minutes later with a worn notepad. She said, "Mrs. Hohenstein, at the time of your surgery and subsequent oncology recommendations, I had already stopped using stem cell replacement chemotherapy on my patients because it had killed so many of them. You, my dear, having not only breast cancer but also MS (even though it had not been diagnosed at the time of my surgery, I had already had my first episode a year earlier), had a doubly compromised immune system. The chemo that was recommended for you would have killed you quickly. God knew your body could not survive that type of treatment. You were very wise to follow His leading."

Over the four years that I saw her, my oncologist became increasingly interested in my story, because I continued to be cancer-free. At one of my appointments, she told me she was scheduled to speak at an oncology convention, and she asked if she could use my file as an example. She wanted to encourage her colleagues to begin listening to their patients that were interested in alternative cancer treatments. She explained to me that doctors don't learn about nutrition in medical school. All they know is treating with pharmaceuticals, so the nutritional approach is foreign to them.

Some doctors are open to learning about it, but the majority of doctors are not. She had several patients, like me, whom she was overseeing; they were, for the most part, doing very well, although none of them were doing the exact same thing. She was anxious to share these patients' stories with her colleagues. I thought it was a great idea!

On my next visit, one year later, she said she had some very positive feedback from her colleagues regarding her presentation. I was thrilled that my story played a small role in that presentation, and I hoped that more doctors would become interested in the benefits of nutrition.

CHAPTER FIFTEEN

Staying Home

In the summer of 2003, I had to quit working because my MS symptoms were worsening, and Kenny and I were both afraid that they would become unmanageable. I was suffering miserably from intense fatigue, and I had an attack that caused my foot to "drop." I had a lot of difficulty walking on my own, so I would sit at my desk and get my paperwork done, but a couple of my coworkers would have to do my running for me (to locate a student or teacher that someone needed, etc.).

One afternoon, as the girls and I were walking to my car to go home, I lost my balance and fell to the ground. Fortunately, we were in a grassy area, so I didn't really hurt myself. My friend, Ralinda, and her two children were walking with us, so she reached down to lift me up, but my legs were so weak, I just fell back to the ground. It took her, her teenage daughter, and Selena to get me standing once again.

I felt so helpless, and I was so embarrassed. When I told Kenny about the incident that night, he said, "You need to give your notice. The school year is almost over, and they will have a few weeks plus the summer to find someone to fill your position. Hopefully, if they find someone quickly, you will be able to train her."

I did give my notice, and fortunately I found someone to replace me and was able to give her some training before the school year ended. I enjoyed staying home so much, and I regained my strength quickly. Kenny was doing a total remodel on a house that we bought to flip, and I was able to get a lot of rest, exercise every day, get all of my housework and cooking done, and still find time to help him with the remodeling job.

I did a lot of painting and running back and forth to Lowes, and I loved it! Once school started back in the fall, I seriously missed being at school with my girls. Fortunately, Selena was going into her senior year and was able to drive herself and Kristen back and forth to school every day. It was a 45-minute drive each way, if the traffic wasn't bad, and they were both still able to be involved in all of the extracurricular activities they both loved.

Selena had been on a competition cheerleading squad for several years. We had so much fun going to her competitions, which were very much like the ones you see on TV. One time during a national competition, one of the girls (not on our team) got her tooth knocked out. You could hear it "ping" across the basketball court. She kept on cheering without skipping a beat as the blood ran down the front of her uniform. Those girls were tough and determined competitors. It was amazing to watch them throw each other around and perform their routines with perfect precision.

Selena decided to opt out of cheerleading her senior year and joined the swim team instead. She had exercise-induced asthma, which didn't seem to bother her too much while cheerleading, but it became an issue with swimming. She was determined to compete, though, and only had one very frightening asthma attack during the season. I was so proud of her stick-to-itiveness, and because I wasn't confined to a job, I was able to go to all of her competitions and even be the team mom. She finished the season much improved in her swimming abilities, and we made some great memories.

My mom was a swim instructor and taught all of her children and grandchildren how to swim before we even learned to walk, but Selena was the only one in our family that was ever on a swim team, and she truly enjoyed it.

Selena and Kristen were both involved in The King's Academy Fine Arts Program which was one of the best in the country. The King's Academy was the first high school to be given permission to perform the Broadway version of *Beauty and the Beast*. Pretty impressive!

Selena and Kristen were both able to perform in programs such as *Sound of Music, Carousel,* and *Les Misérables.*

The performances were so professionally done, they felt like, looked like, and sounded like Broadway productions. Those were some awesome opportunities and learning experiences, and the girls made amazing memories with their school friends. Their director, David Schneider, had a huge impact on their lives. He even taught his students to appreciate opera. Selena and Kristen's love for Andrea Bocelli, Charlotte Church, Sarah Brightman, and Josh Groban rubbed off on Kenny and me. We gained some culture that we never anticipated.

CHAPTER SIXTEEN
Moving to Ocala

It was the summer of 2004, and several things were happening simultaneously when we decided to consider moving to Gainesville or Ocala in North Central Florida. Kenny was unexpectedly laid off from a supervisory position at the concrete company where he had been working for about a year, and although he had been searching high and low for employment, there was nothing to be found. Selena had graduated from King's Academy and was on her senior trip to Europe. Selena had also just been accepted to the University of Florida in Gainesville. On top of all that, the real estate bubble that had been rapidly growing for several years in our country was about to burst.

I was riding my exercise bike one Friday morning and praying about Kenny's job situation, when the Lord prompted me to ask Kenny to apply for a job at the University of Florida. After I finished my bike ride and prayer time, I went to ask Kenny how he might feel about applying at the maintenance and building department of UF.

He said, "That sounds interesting. I guess we could see what they have available online."

So, we went online and, sure enough, there were a couple of jobs available in that department. We filled out the applications and made plans to go up and look around the following day.

Because Selena was going to be living on campus in Gainesville, and Kenny might be working there also, we decided to look for homes in Ocala which was 45 minutes south of Gainesville. We wanted Selena to be able to exercise her independence without feeling that we were hovering over her, yet we would be close enough to get to her quickly if she needed anything. We were also hoping that UF would be Kristen's college of choice, so we would be equally accessible to her. Plus, Kenny and I really weren't interested in living in a college town.

It just so happened that Natalie Lyons, my friend from Cornerstone, had moved to Ocala several years earlier. She had come to visit us a week or so earlier and had brought a real estate magazine from Ocala with her. She laid it on the kitchen counter when she arrived and said, "I have no idea why I brought this, but I enjoy looking through these magazines every once in a while, just for fun. I thought you might enjoy it, too." That magazine was still lying on the kitchen counter right where she put it.

When I opened it up, it fell open to the center page that had all the realtors listed that were advertising in the magazine. I noticed this sweet-looking couple in the middle of the page and said, "Kenny, I think I'm going to call them and see if they have any availability to show us around Ocala tomorrow."

He said, "Sounds good to me."

I called, and the wife answered the phone and said, surprisingly enough, that her schedule was completely open the next morning. I told her we could meet her around 10 a.m.

Before we arrived in Ocala, Kenny and I had already decided we wanted to look at new construction. When we met with the realtor, we told her what we were interested in, and she took us to several new developments. We walked through numerous model homes, but couldn't find any floor plans that we both liked.

Kristen was with us, and she was so unhappy at the thought of moving and leaving all of her friends that she couldn't find anything positive in this new adventure. My heart was truly aching for her, but after seeing the incredible difference in the price of housing between Ocala and West Palm Beach, we knew this was a move we needed to make. Since Kenny was looking for work and we didn't know if anything would pan out with his UF applications, we were interested in flipping houses.

Most of the housing in Ocala was about half the price of comparable homes in South Florida. We had a line of credit on our West Palm Beach house that would enable us to "pay cash" for a house in Ocala while we waited to sell our house in West Palm Beach. Once our West Palm Beach house sold, we could then get a line of credit on our Ocala home that would enable us to purchase another house to flip.

After looking at new construction for a couple of hours, we decided to take a break. We picked up some lunch to take back to the realtor's office so we could look at some real estate magazines while we ate. We hadn't been there for more than five minutes when Kristen said, "What about this house?" She passed the magazine to Kenny, and he said, "Oh, yeah. I like that one."

He asked the realtor, "What do you know about this neighborhood, Quail Hollow?"

The realtor said, "Oh, that is a very nice area. I think you would love it."

So Kenny said, "Can you see if we can get in to see this house today?"

"Sure," she said, as she headed to the telephone.

We finished up our lunch, and a few minutes later we were on our way to Quail Hollow. When we pulled into the development, I said, "Oh my, I love this neighborhood. I don't care what the house looks like; I want to live here!" Then we pulled up to the house, and I said with even more enthusiasm, "Oh my, I love this house! It doesn't matter what it looks like on the inside, Kenny can make it beautiful if it isn't already."

When we went inside, we saw that the house did need some work, but it was a beautiful home on a very nice lot with a gorgeous screened-in pool area. I knew Kenny could make it our dream home. So we went back to the realtor's office, made an offer, it was accepted, and we bought the house. As we started to make the four-hour drive back home, I said, "Kenny, let's go back by the house and look at it one more time before we leave. I know we can't go back inside, but I just want to see it again."

He said, "Sure, I would like to do that."

So a few minutes later, as we were sitting in front of the house taking it all in, my cell phone rang. It was Selena calling from Europe. I answered the phone and Selena said, "Hey, Mom. What are you doing?" I said, "Your dad and Kristen and I are sitting in front of the house we just bought in Ocala. What are you doing?"

She said, "WHAT? I leave for a few days to go on my senior trip, and you buy a house in Ocala without even telling me you were thinking about it?"

I had to laugh. We hadn't talked to her in a couple of days, and all of this had transpired in a little more than 24 hours. So I tried to bring her up to date as quickly as possible as it was an international call. She did have time to tell us that she was in Austria and that the views were breathtaking, but she was still stunned when we hung up.

That was the end of May 2004. We came home, put our house up for sale, and began packing. We had plans to attend a family reunion in Daytona Beach on the Fourth of July weekend. Selena had been back from her senior trip for several weeks by then, so we were able to go together as a family. We had a wonderful time. On our last day there, a friend who had been taking care of our pets called to say that someone had vandalized our house and Kenny's truck, so we headed home a day early.

Fortunately, nothing was missing inside our home, but someone had taken a jagged rock and scratched the paint on Kenny's truck all the way around from top to bottom, smashed our beautiful leaded glass front door with the rock, and then thrown the rock through one of the bedroom windows. We were really upset that someone would do something like that, but we were so thankful that nothing was stolen, and it wasn't a life-changing event.

Kenny made the repairs, and we moved to Ocala at the end of July while Kristen, Selena, and my mom were on a mission trip to Russia. This was one busy summer! We had a lot of people come by our house in West Palm, but nobody had put in an offer yet. We had really hoped to have it sold before we moved, but it was in God's hands.

Kenny and I loved Ocala. There is an amazing difference between North Central Florida and South Florida. North Central Florida has rolling hills, four seasons, azaleas, crepe myrtles, dogwood trees, all kinds of beautiful flowering plants, and trees that I had never seen before. South Florida is flat and hot, and there are no seasons except for summer (in my opinion). Most of the trees are palm trees, which are beautiful, but I had seen enough of them.

Kristen and Selena hated Ocala because it was small, and they had never lived in a small town before. When we moved there, Ocala had one mall (and basically still does), one theater, and no beaches (wait...what?). It was pure culture shock for the girls; but it didn't matter as much to Selena because she was going to be starting college and living in Gainesville in a few short weeks.

Although Gainesville isn't much bigger than Ocala, it is a college town and has much more to offer a young person in the way of entertainment and social activities. However, the fact that her scholastic breaks wouldn't be spent with West Palm Beach friends made Selena quite unhappy.

Kristen was completely devastated. Her friends were all in West Palm Beach and attending The King's Academy, which had so much more to offer than the school she would be attending in Ocala. If we had stayed in West Palm Beach, Kristen would be going into ninth grade with all of her buddies from the past four years, but instead she was going into ninth grade with no friends. It was terribly difficult for her and a very trying time for Kenny and me.

In conjunction with helping Kristen adjust and processing the stress of the move in general, I went through the worst MS attack that I had ever experienced: I lost sight in my right eye. In order to get from one end of the house to the other, I had to use the wall for support, and even that was exhausting. I suffered from intense numbness in most of my body, except my head.

My legs were especially problematic. The only way to describe the difficulty is that I felt like fireballs were moving up and down the nerves of my legs. I couldn't sleep because of the discomfort. I've had minor problems with my back for many years, but those aches and pains were intensified during this attack. I was miserable, to say the least.

A few weeks before we left West Palm Beach to move to Ocala, I had my annual "female" check-up. According to the results of my pelvic ultrasound, a large mass was discovered on one of my ovaries. Because we were in the midst of packing, trying to sell our West Palm Beach house, and running back and forth to Ocala to finalize the purchase of our new house, I didn't have time to follow up on this large ovarian mass. But, I can assure you, the thought of it never left my mind.

To top it off, a little over a month after we moved into our new home, two hurricanes came through Ocala. The first one put a huge limb through our roof right above Kristen's bedroom. Because of the heavy rains, her ceiling collapsed, her room was flooded, and the brand new carpet that had just been laid a few weeks before was ruined. That didn't help her mood much.

Two weeks later, the second hurricane ripped through Ocala, uprooting a large tree in our backyard that completely crushed our very large pool enclosure. The tree and most of the screen room ended up in the pool. One of those hurricanes also badly damaged the roof of our West Palm Beach house, which had just come under contract, but the sale had not been finalized. Fortunately, the buyers still wanted the house. After several trips running back and forth to West Palm Beach to clean up the mess, make repairs, and find a roofing contractor, we were able to close a few weeks later with some adjustments to the original agreement.

Shortly after we sold our West Palm Beach house, the real estate bubble burst, and the housing market came crashing down. If it weren't for God's timing in our move and the sale of our house, we would have been "up a creek" financially.

Many things were contributors to the MS attack that began shortly after we moved to Ocala: the damage to both of our homes; the stress of the move;

the sale of our house; my concern for Kristen's emotional welfare; and the awareness of this large ovarian cyst, to name a few.

Our wonderful new next-door neighbor, Judy, recommended a primary care doctor to me. I was able to get an appointment quickly. The nurse practitioner that I saw listened intently to my history, and although he thought nutrition was a farce, he did share with me that his wife was getting a measure of relief from her serious female problems through some supplements prescribed by an ob-gyn in town who had begun specializing in nutrition. The nurse practitioner didn't understand it, and he wasn't going to be convinced by his wife's case alone, but he was more than happy to recommend this doctor to me, since I needed an ob-gyn to check further into my ovarian mass.

The ob-gyn did several different types of blood work on me, most of which targeted hormone levels in the body. Once he was able to see what my hormones were doing, he prescribed supplements that would bring troubling hormone levels back into balance. It was expensive, but once my hormones were back where they were supposed to be, that large mass just disappeared.

CHAPTER SEVENTEEN
Treating Multiple Sclerosis

Balancing my hormones also helped my MS symptoms. My doctor's first priority was the ovarian mass, but once that was gone, he addressed the MS symptoms more specifically. I believe the most beneficial supplement I have ever taken for MS is vitamin D3. He told me that recent studies had shown that one common denominator among patients with MS is that most seem to have a vitamin D3 deficiency. He recommended 4000 IU a day. Once I began taking that, my symptoms began improving. Most of them either disappeared or became manageable again.

Since I started on Vitamin D3 nearly ten years ago, I have not had another MS attack. I have had symptoms that come and go or worsen and then get better, but I've not had another debilitating attack. MS attacks for most people are stress-induced; I can honestly say I have had plenty of stress in the past ten years, but I've been blessed to avoid another MS attack.

I also exercise for at least 30 minutes, 5 days a week. I know that has been an important part of maintaining my health. My sister Donna and I used to walk for 30 minutes and then do Tae Bo for 30 minutes, five days a week. I developed heel spurs and had to give up walking for exercise, but I still do Tae Bo.

It is important for everyone to find some form of exercise that they can do consistently that is enjoyable to them. I highly recommend walking because almost everyone can do that, and it is free, except for the initial purchase of some good walking shoes.

I also visit my chiropractor for adjustments at least once a month, more if I'm feeling stressed or experiencing more discomfort than usual. Those visits help me tremendously.

As I mentioned earlier, I am a perfectionist or slightly obsessive-compulsive. My friends and family may say it's a little more than "slightly," but however you want to view it, I spend a lot of time and energy trying to do things perfectly and keeping my home and surroundings spotless and everything in its place. Because of these tendencies, I overwork myself and very rarely sit down to rest. I always see something that needs to be done and many times end up overdoing it. When this happens, I experience repercussions.

I exacerbate my MS and struggle with pain and spasticity in my legs, among other things. Then I get discouraged and wonder what's going to happen to me in the future when I'm not as strong as I am now, not able to accomplish all the things I want to accomplish, and need my family to take care of me, rather than my being able to take care of them. Then I have to remind myself that God only gives us grace for today.

God doesn't want us worrying about the future. When we do that, we are seeing ourselves dealing with those future problems in our own strength. In reality, if and when we get there, He is going to be there giving us grace and strength and possibly even removing those obstacles that we fear. We have no idea how He may intervene. So, I'm trying to learn to take one day at a time. We've all heard that phrase a gazillion times, but it happens to be full of truth. Being true, however, doesn't prevent it from being hard to live by.

Don't get me wrong. I believe we need to plan for the future and be wise, but there is no place in our lives for worry and fear. "For God has not given us a spirit of fear, but of power and of love and of a sound mind" (2 Timothy 1:7, NKJV).

We have to spend time with Him, though, to be able to apply this verse successfully. I try to spend some quiet time in God's Word and in prayer each morning. It prepares me for the day.

The most wonderful devotional I have ever come across is *Jesus Calling: Enjoying Peace in His Presence,* by Sarah Young. It speaks volumes to me every day. I have bought so many of them for friends and family members and for people who are going through a difficult time. It seems to bless everyone who uses it.

I also try to read a chapter of Proverbs each day. Proverbs has 31 chapters, so there is one for every day of the month, and I never tire of reading them, over and over again. Since Proverbs is the book of wisdom, I tend to see something new in each chapter every time I read it. I don't know about you, but I need as much wisdom as I can get. My favorite is Proverbs 31:10-31, which is the description of a virtuous woman. She sounds more like a superhero than a mere human, but she is someone that I want to strive to become.

I also like to read through the Bible, just one chapter a day. It takes a while to get through the whole Bible that way, but that's all right. When I'm done, I simply start over.

Find a prayer partner or an accountability partner. That's someone you can share your heart with, who will be honest with you when you are off course, and who will cheer you on if you need to take a leap of faith. My sister Sandy and I talk every morning, and we pray together, for each other, for our families, and for any difficulties that we or they may be facing.

I want to encourage you to take control of your physical health and your spiritual well-being. They go hand in hand. Eat lots of fruits and vegetables. Drink lots of purified water. Stay away from chemicals to the best of your ability. Get plenty of exercise and plenty of rest. Learn to say no to unnecessary stressors in your life. Spend time with the Lord each day and learn to lean on Him and follow His leading in your life. Nobody can take care of *you* like you can. This is the only life you have. Treasure it.

I almost forgot to come full circle with Kenny's University of Florida applications. He didn't get a job there; in fact, we never heard back from them at all. Instead, soon after we settled into our Ocala home, Kenny walked over to the housing development on the east side of ours and applied for a construction superintendent job. They hired him on the spot. So, in my estimation, applying for a job at UF was just God's way of turning our hearts toward Ocala. Funny how He works.

CHAPTER EIGHTEEN

The Power of Fasting

When I was around sixteen years old, we received a call from my mom's family in Alabama, informing us that that my second cousin, Christy, had cancer. She was only four or five at the time, but she had a very large tumor in her abdomen attached to many of her organs. The doctors were going to have to remove much of her stomach, intestines, and parts of some other organs. The doctors said that if she survived, she would never be able to have children.

My mother began fasting for Christy and praying for God's healing on her little life—but more importantly, praying for His perfect will for Christy.

That is my first memory of my mother fasting. I remember thinking, "Wow! What a sacrifice to not eat anything and drink only water for several days!" I was interested to see what God was going to do with this.

When my mom began fasting, she asked the Lord to tell her when to stop. On the night of the seventh day of her fast she had a dream. In that dream, she heard a song that started softly and then got louder and louder. The song was one she had taught the neighborhood children in her Bible study. The words are, "Done, Done, <u>D</u> <u>O</u> <u>N</u> <u>E</u>. Done, Done, Done perfectly!"

The song is actually about Jesus' finished work on the cross as He died for our sins, but my mom she was "done" fasting and that Christy was healed.

Jump to thirty-eight years after that event, to the present day: Christy is alive and well, and she has three children of her own—by natural childbirth, not adoption. To this day, she has not had a recurrence of cancer.

God honors fasting and prayer. That doesn't mean that He will always give us what we want, but it opens the door for Him to show His glory in amazing ways. More importantly it opens our eyes to *see* His glory.

Because of my mom's example, I have fasted on many occasions for my children when I felt like I needed to do more than pray. I felt the need to offer that sacrifice to God and then leave the outcome to Him. He has always done more than I hoped for and has allowed me to experience His grace on a deeper level because of the sacrifice that I made through fasting.

I worry, which is sinful, but fasting comforts me. I know that I'm powerless to control anything in this life; but when I give circumstances and people to the

Lord, through fasting and prayer, I know that He will do something special, both in their lives and in mine. It is an awesome thing. I highly recommend it.

During the 2012 presidential election, I fasted for two specific reasons: first, for Election Day. I was involved in "40 Days of Prayer and Fasting" with my church and many churches across the country for this very critical election.

Second, I was fasting for my mom. On Election Day she was scheduled for a stereotactic biopsy of a lump and also two areas of calcifications in her right breast. After all of the fasting she had done for me through the years, it was now my turn to fast for her healing and God's perfect will for her life.

During my quiet time one morning, I was reminded of something I had recently read that went like this: "After all of the time you have given to prayer and fasting over the last 40 days, if tomorrow's election doesn't go your way, will you still love God, or will you be angry with Him?"

As I was contemplating that, and simultaneously praying fervently for my mom, I had to apply that same question to the outcome of my mom's biopsy. Will I still love God if my mom's biopsy is malignant, or will I be angry with Him?

As I was praying that I would accept His will graciously, no matter the outcome, I felt God say to me, "Terry, you don't have to get *your* way, no matter how righteous it may seem, for me to have *My* way. Regardless of the outcome, I am in control."

No matter how "good" my way may seem and no matter how right my heart is with God as I'm praying for what seems to me to be "righteous" and/or "best," ultimately God's way is perfect. I need to humbly pray as Jesus did, "Not my will, but yours be done." Only after I submit my will to His can He truly work in my life, enabling me to accept His plan, whatever that may be. He can then give me the strength to walk through whatever the future holds.

My Mom's biopsies were malignant, but the breast cancer that she had was not aggressive or invasive. It certainly wasn't the same cancer that I had, and she is doing great. She feels very healthy and looks wonderful, and my sister Sandy, who is her caregiver, makes sure she eats healthfully, exercises, and takes good supplements.

When circumstances look grim and may even appear to be hopeless, I love to read the biblical story of Esther. What an amazing story of miraculous intervention through incredible twists and turns! If you have never read it, please treat yourself. It will help you understand that God has no limitations. He can intervene in our lives when circumstances appear hopeless. Nothing is impossible for Him. *He can make a way where there seems to be no way.*

Whatever you may be dealing with today, I hope you can find comfort in knowing that God is still on

His throne, and He is in complete control. Nothing that may come your way, today or any day in the future, is a surprise to God. He's always there, and He wants to carry you through it.

I love the illustration of the tapestry—we see the tapestry of our lives from the back, with all of its messy threads and knots; but God sees the tapestry from the front, beautifully woven and perfect. No matter how ugly or fragmented our lives may seem to us at any given moment, God is constantly working in the background to make a beautiful tapestry of our lives. He can bring beauty from ashes. Let Him have His way.

I want to challenge you and myself (especially) to love Him and trust Him no matter what. He has promised that His grace is sufficient to keep you wherever He may lead you. May God richly bless you as you endeavor to follow Him.

About the Cover

by Kristen Hohenstein

When I was presented with the opportunity to go to Haiti this summer with my church, I immediately knew it was something I wanted to do. My reasons weren't honorable. My main desire wasn't for God to work through me or to do some kingdom building. I wanted to travel; I didn't want to spend the entire summer in Gainesville without seeing a glimpse of the outside world. The fact that I would be on a mission trip "doing good" was a plus. I love other cultures. I've spent the last two summers living in Russia, and I wanted a taste of something else. I knew I would enjoy Haiti and its people, but I wasn't expecting to fall in love. Russia has a big piece of my heart, but it's a hardened piece of my heart. Russia is not an easy place to love. While there, I built walls to defend myself against some of the heartbreaking things I saw. I was tired of crying, and it was the only way I could cope with the things I couldn't do anything about. I didn't want to be affected by the overwhelming sense of hopelessness that seemed to follow around every corner.

Six months after signing up for the Haiti trip, I was flying over the Caribbean only a few minutes away from touching down on Haitian soil. I was nervous. We were flying into Port au Prince. During the whole flight, I was mentally preparing myself for the devastation I would be seeing. I'd been warned about rubble, the smell, and the trash that would be piled up everywhere you looked. In the months leading up to this trip, I prayed that God would soften my heart that I had hardened over the last few years as a defense mechanism against my feelings. I needed Him to help me be vulnerable by tearing down the walls I built in Russia to keep the sadness out.

As soon as we landed, I could feel God working in my heart. Those hardened pieces began to melt away. I felt warm and exhilarated. Port au Prince wasn't our final destination. Once we met up with our guide and police escort, we got in our van and began the journey to our destination, the town of Bohoc.

Driving through Port au Prince was exciting. People paid no mind to traffic laws. If there was a sidewalk nearby, it was just another lane you could use to get around the car in front of you. There wasn't as much rubble as I had expected. Trash didn't line the streets. We drove past a couple of tent cities that sprang up after the earthquake. Then we drove past a new block of apartment buildings being built for people who lost their homes in that same earthquake. Five long hours and a couple of uncomfortable bathroom breaks later, we reached what would be our home for the next week. I never could have imagined the work God would do in my heart while I stayed in this little town.

Our first night there, we met with Bohoc's leadership council. It's comprised of a few men and women who keep the town running and decide what missionaries will do when they come for a visit. What an amazing group of people. They welcomed us with the warmth and enthusiasm of a loving family. We went around and introduced ourselves, got debriefed on what we would be doing, and settled in for a night of rest after our long day of travel.

The week that followed was amazing. I could probably write twenty pages about my experiences, but the underlying theme of each one would be the hope you find in God's love. We went to church, spent time in orphanages, helped a family build a pit latrine, and taught conversational English. With each encounter, I realized I needed these people more than they needed me.

The first time I came to this realization was in church the Sunday after our arrival. On our way there, I prayed that God would work in my heart during the sermon despite the language barrier. God is good and answered my prayer twofold. Our guide ended up sitting right behind me and translated the sermon about Abraham and Isaac. But what moved me was the realization that while we were worshiping with our Haitian brothers and sisters, our church back home was doing the same thing. While the choir sang, I began to cry. It was so beautiful and clear. I could feel the Holy Spirit moving as their voices rang throughout the church. Having the sermon translated as the pastor spoke was wonderful, but the tears I cried that morning were the real answer to my prayer. God was working in the hardened places of my heart that I had been keeping in the dark — untouched for years.

Over the following days, God continued to meet my worries with His grace. Matthew 28 is the name of the orphanage we worked in while we stayed in Bohoc. I don't really know what to do with children. I'm introverted and these little human beings who are so full of energy and need every ounce of your attention intimidate me and make me tired. I prayed that if there was a child who just needed to be quietly held and loved, God would send him/her to me. Within five minutes of arriving at Matthew 28, I met Colinda. She was a shy little girl who was watching me from the gazebo as the other kids ran around playing soccer or jump rope. Once she noticed that I was looking back at her with a smile, she warmed up to me. Two hours later, she was asleep in my arms. I grew up in a wonderful, loving family. I never lacked affection or affirmation of my parents' love for me. My heart was breaking as she slept. When was the last time someone held her? When was the last time she felt safe and protected? In that moment, I knew that the reason I came to Haiti was for the few hours I got to hold this little girl, letting her know that she was loved. I don't know if she will remember me or if she will still be in

Bohoc when I return next summer, but I will always find joy in the thought that she might carry those few hours of comfort with her.

God continued to wake my heart up each day. Every person I met was a gift. The family we built the pit latrine with had a sweet little boy named Peter. Peter was eight years old and about the size of a large watermelon with limbs. His arms were tiny and his legs were curved in permanent cross-legged style. When you are born with a deformity in Haiti, you are usually tossed aside. Life isn't easy, and you have to be able to survive its hardships on your own. Seeing the love this family had for their son was overwhelming. Seeing the way his brothers took breaks during their games of catch to hug him was enough to put a smile on my face for a long time. But what amazed me the most about Peter was that, despite his circumstances, he smiled, he laughed, he posed for goofy pictures and carried on conversations as if he understood exactly what you were saying. When he saw the bag of nail polish we brought, he summoned me over so he could paint my nails. Then he painted everyone's nails—including the men. Two weeks later, I still have remnants of the manicure he gave me.

I could tell more stories, be more specific. God showed himself to me in so many ways through so many different people. But there is only one message I want to get across. When you live your life in Christ, there is hope. For some reason, the people of Bohoc,

Haiti, have a much better grasp on this reality than I do. You can see it in their faces and hear it in their voices when they talk about God's grace and how good He is. Why is it that I have so much more material to my name than any of them, but the amount of joy they have surpasses mine? They don't have air conditioning, they don't have Starbucks, a lot of them ride donkeys as their main mode of transportation. They have so little, but are rich in ways I want to be.

There are pieces of my past that I've allowed to become heavy chains around my heart, weighing me down as I walk through life. These things have lived in the untouched, hardened parts of my heart. The truth about those walls I finished building in Russia is that I began construction on them about a year before my first summer in Moscow. I was tired of being sad and feeling hopeless because of the disappointing things I had done. I wanted a way to keep those feelings out. I've been a Christian since I was a little girl, but I didn't want to make myself vulnerable to Christ. I was ashamed of who I had become. I tried to hide my heart from God even though He knew what was there all along. It's only through God's grace that these walls of mine began to crumble. He started chipping away at them as soon as I was willing to let Him. A few months later, I was sitting in church listening to my pastor talk about an upcoming trip to Bohoc, Haiti.

The people of Bohoc drove a bulldozer right through the remnants of the walls that were still "guarding" my heart. They showed me that joy isn't circumstantial, because Christ's love isn't circumstantial. In Christ, there is hope no matter where you live, what you have done, or what the world has done to you. Yes, there will be hard times. You will be disappointed, and you will be the disappointment. You will hurt, but this hurt isn't eternal. Christ's love is eternal.

When most people think of Haiti, they think of poverty, corruption, and sorrow. These things are all true. But the little community of Bohoc changed the way I look at Haiti. There is hope. There is beauty everywhere you look. Things will get better because they know God will keep His promises to provide. More importantly, they changed the way I look at God and my circumstances. Christ used Bohoc and the people I met there to change my heart.

The flight back from Haiti to Miami was the worst flight I have ever experienced. At one point, the turbulence was so bad that everyone on the plane screamed, and I thought the plane was going down. I was scared. I even cried a couple of times. I prayed that God would get us home safely, but I wasn't trusting that He would. How easy it is to go back to our old ways. When the pilot finally announced our descent, I looked out the window. I'll never forget what I saw. God is good. He keeps His promises. He is hope.

"For I am convinced that neither death nor life, neither angels nor demons, neither the present nor the future, nor any powers, neither height nor depth, nor anything else in all creation, will be able to separate us from the love of God that is in Christ Jesus our Lord" *(Romans 8:38-39, NIV).*

Kristen Hohenstein